Eat for Health

The Essential Recipe Handbook

Publisher's Note:
Raw or semi-cooked eggs should not be consumed by babies, toddlers, pregnant women,
the elderly or those suffering from recurring illness.

This is a **STAR FIRE** book
First edition published in 2006

Publisher and Creative Director: Nick Wells
Project Editor: Cat Emslie
Photographers: Paul Forrester, Colin Bowling and Stephen Brayne
Home Economists & Stylists: Jaqueline Bellefontaine, Mandy Phipps,
Vicki Smallwood and Penny Stephens
Art Director: Mike Spender
Layout Design: Dave Jones
Digital Design and Production: Chris Herbert
Proofreader: Dawn Laker

08 10 12 11 09

1 3 5 7 9 10 8 6 4 2

This edition first published 2008 by
STAR FIRE
Crabtree Hall, Crabtree Lane
Fulham, London SW6 6TY
United Kingdom

www.star-fire.co.uk

Star Fire is part of the Foundry Creative Media Co. Ltd
© 2008 The Foundry Creative Media Co. Ltd

ISBN 978-1-84786-258-7

Printed in China

Eat for Health

The Essential Recipe Handbook

General Editor: Gina Steer

STAR FIRE

Contents

Nutrition: The Role of Essential Nutrients

A healthy and well-balanced diet is the body's primary energy source. In children, it constitutes the building blocks for future health as well as providing lots of energy. In adults, it encourages self-healing and regeneration within the body. A well-balanced diet will provide the body with all the essential nutrients it needs. This can be achieved by eating a variety of foods, demonstrated in the pyramid below.

FATS

PROTEINS

milk, yogurt   meat, fish, poultry,
and cheese   eggs, nuts and pulses

FRUITS AND VEGETABLES

STARCHY CARBOHYDRATES

cereals, potatoes, bread, rice and pasta

FATS

Fats fall into two categories: saturated and unsaturated. Fats are an essential part of the diet as they are a source of energy and provide essential fatty acids and fat-soluble vitamins, but it is very important that a healthy balance is achieved. The right balance should boost the body's immunity to infection and keep muscles, nerves and arteries in good condition. Saturated fats are of animal origin and can be found in dairy produce, meat, eggs, margarines and hard white cooking fat (lard) as well as in manufactured products such as pies, biscuits and cakes. A high intake of saturated fat over many years has been proven to increase heart disease and high blood cholesterol levels and often leads to weight gain. Lowering the amount of saturated fat that we consume is very important, but this does not mean that it is good to consume lots of other types of fat.

There are two kinds of unsaturated fats: polyunsaturated and monounsaturated. Polyunsaturated fats include safflower, soybean, corn and sesame oils. The Omega-3 oils in polyunsaturated fats have been found to be beneficial to coronary health and can encourage brain growth and development. They are derived from oily fish such as salmon, mackerel, herring, pilchards and sardines. It is recommended that we should eat these types of fish at least once a week. Alternative liver oil supplements are also available. The most popular oils that are high in monounsaturates are olive oil, sunflower oil and peanut oil. Monounsaturated fats are also known to help reduce the levels of cholestrol.

PROTEINS

Composed of amino acids – proteins' building blocks – proteins perform a wide variety of essential functions for the body, including supplying energy and building and repairing tissues. Good sources of proteins are eggs, milk, yogurt, cheese, meat, fish, poultry, eggs, nuts and pulses. (See the second level of the pyramid.) Some of these foods, however, contain saturated fats. To strike a nutritional balance, eat generous amounts of vegetable protein foods such as soya, beans, lentils, peas and nuts.

MINERALS

CALCIUM Important for healthy bones and teeth, nerve transmission, muscle contraction, blood clotting and hormone function. Also promotes a healthy heart and skin, relieves aching muscles and bones, maintains the correct acid–alkaline balance and reduces menstrual cramps. Good sources are dairy products, small bones of small fish, nuts, pulses, fortified white flours, breads and green leafy vegetables.

CHROMIUM Chromium balances blood sugar levels, helps to reduce cravings, improves lifespan, helps protect DNA and is essential for heart function. Good sources are brewer's yeast, wholemeal bread, rye bread, oysters, potatoes, green peppers, butter and parsnips.

IODINE Important for the manufacture of thyroid hormones and for normal development. Good sources are seafood, seaweed, milk and dairy.

IRON As a component of haemoglobin, iron carries oxygen around the body. It is vital for normal growth and development. Good sources are liver, corned beef, red meat, fortified breakfast cereals, pulses, green leafy vegetables, egg yolk, cocoa and cocoa products.

MAGNESIUM Important for efficient functioning of metabolic enzymes and development of the skeleton. Magnesium promotes healthy muscles by helping them to relax and is therefore good for PMS. It is also important for heart muscles and the nervous system. Good sources are nuts, green vegetables, meat, cereals, milk and yogurt.

PHOSPHORUS Forms and maintains bones and teeth, builds muscle tissue, helps maintain pH of the body and aids metabolism and energy production. Phosphorus is present in almost all foods.

POTASSIUM Enables processing of nutrients; promotes healthy nerves and muscles; maintains fluid balance; helps secretion of insulin for blood sugar control; relaxes muscles; maintains heart functioning and stimulates gut movement. Good sources are fruit, vegetables, milk and bread.

SELENIUM Antioxidant properties help to protect against free radicals and carcinogens. Selenium reduces inflammation, stimulates the immune system, promotes a healthy heart and helps vitamin E's action. Necessary for the male reproductive system and for metabolism. Good sources are tuna, liver, kidney, meat, eggs, cereals, nuts and dairy products.

SODIUM Important in helping to control body fluid, preventing dehydration. Sodium is involved in muscle and nerve function and helps move nutrients into cells. All foods are good sources. Processed, pickled and salted foods are richest in sodium but should be eaten in moderation.

ZINC Important for metabolism and healing; aids ability to cope with stress; promotes a healthy nervous system and brain, especially in the growing foetus; aids bone and teeth formation and is essential for energy. Good sources are liver, meat, pulses, whole–grain cereals, nuts and oysters.

VITAMINS

VITAMIN A Important for cell growth and developmemt and for the formation of visual pigments in the eye. Vitamin A comes in two forms: retinol and beta–carotenes. Retinol is found in liver, meat and whole milk. Beta–carotene is a powerful antioxidant and is found in red and yellow fruits and vegetables such as carrots, mangoes and apricots.

VITAMIN B1 Important in releasing energy from carbohydrate-containing foods. Good sources are yeast and yeast products, bread, fortified breakfast cereals and potatoes.

VITAMIN B2 Important for metabolism of proteins, fats and carbohydrates to produce energy. Good sources are meat, yeast extracts, fortified breakfast cereals and milk and its products.

VITAMIN B3 Required for the metabolism of food into energy. Good sources are milk, fortified cereals, pulses, meat, poultry and eggs.

VITAMIN B5 Important for the metabolism of food and energy production. All foods are good sources but especially fortified breakfast cereals, whole–grain bread and dairy products.

VITAMIN B6 Important for metabolism of protein and fat. Vitamin B6 may also be involved in the regulation of sex hormones. Good sources are liver, fish, pork, soya beans and peanuts.

VITAMIN B12 Important for the production of red blood cells and DNA. It is vital for growth and the nervous system. Good sources are meat, fish, eggs, poultry and milk.

BIOTIN Important for metabolism of fatty acids. Good sources of biotin are liver, kidney, eggs and nuts.

VITAMIN C Important for healing wounds and the formation of collagen which keeps skin and bones strong. It is an important antioxidant. Good sources are fruits, especially soft summer fruits, and vegetables.

VITAMIN D Important for absorption and handling of calcium to help build bone strength. Good sources are oily fish, eggs, whole milk and milk products, margarine and of course sufficient exposure to sunlight, as vitamin D is made in the skin.

VITAMIN E Important as an antioxidant vitamin helping to protect cell membranes from damage. Good sources are vegetable oils, margarines, seeds, nuts and green vegetables.

FOLIC ACID Critical during pregnancy for the development of the brain and nerves. It is always essential for brain and nerve function and is needed for utilising protein and red blood cell formation. Good sources are whole–grain cereals, fortified cereals, green leafy vegetables, oranges and liver.

VITAMIN K Important for controlling blood clotting. Good sources are cauliflower, Brussels sprouts, lettuce, cabbage, beans, broccoli, peas, asparagus, potatoes, corn oil, tomatoes and milk.

CARBOHYDRATES

Carbohydrates are an energy source and come in two forms: starch and sugar. Starch carbohydrates are also known as complex carbohydrates and they include all cereals, potatoes, breads, rice and pasta. Eating whole–grain varieties of these foods also provides fibre. Diets high in fibre are believed to be beneficial in helping to prevent bowel cancer and keep cholesterol down. Sugar carbohydrates – also known as fast-release because they provide a quick fix of energy – include sugar and sugar-sweetened products. Other sugars are lactose (from milk) and fructose (from fruit).

High Fibre

Fibre is essential for a healthy lifestyle and diets that are low in fibre lead to constipation and bowel disorders. It is recommended that we eat 24 g of fibre per day to retain a healthy lifestyle. The following recipes are designed to help you get as much fibre into your diet as possible in delicious and interesting ways.

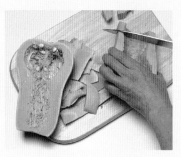 

Cream of Pumpkin Soup

1. Cut the skinned and deseeded pumpkin flesh into 2.5 cm/1 inch cubes. Heat the olive oil in a large saucepan and cook the pumpkin for 2–3 minutes, coating it completely with oil. Chop the onion and leek finely and cut the carrot and celery into small cubes.

2. Add the vegetables to the saucepan with the garlic and cook, stirring, for 5 minutes, or until they have begun to soften. Cover the vegetables with the water and bring to the boil. Season with plenty of salt and pepper and the nutmeg, then cover and simmer for 15–20 minutes, or until all of the vegetables are tender.

3. When the vegetables are tender, remove from the heat, cool slightly then pour into a food processor or blender. Liquidise to form a smooth purée then pass through a sieve into a clean saucepan.

4. Adjust the seasoning to taste and add all but 2 tablespoons of the cream and enough water to obtain the correct consistency. Bring the soup to boiling point, add the cayenne pepper and serve immediately swirled with cream.

Ingredients   SERVES 4

900 g/2 lb pumpkin flesh (after peeling and discarding the seeds)
4 tbsp olive oil
1 large onion, peeled
1 leek, trimmed
1 carrot, peeled
2 celery sticks
4 garlic cloves, peeled and crushed
1.7 litres/3 pints water
salt and freshly ground black pepper
$1/4$ tsp freshly grated nutmeg
150 ml/$1/4$ pint single cream
$1/4$ tsp cayenne pepper

Nutritional details per 100 g energy 62 kcals/260 kj • protein 2 g • carbohydrate 8 g • fat 3 g • fibre 1.3 g • sugar 2.5 g • sodium 0.1 g

cow's milk-free ✓ egg-free ✓ gluten-free ✓ wheat-free ✓ nut-free ✓ vegetarian vegan ✓ seafood-free

Aduki Bean & Rice Burgers

1 Heat 1 tablespoon of the oil in a saucepan and gently cook the onion for 10 minutes until soft. Add the garlic and curry paste and cook for a few more seconds. Stir in the rice and beans.

2 Pour in the stock, bring to the boil and simmer for 12 minutes, or until all the stock has been absorbed – do not lift the lid for the first 10 minutes of cooking. Reserve.

3 Lightly mash the tofu. Add to the rice mixture with the garam masala, coriander, salt and pepper. Mix.

4 Divide the mixture into eight and shape into burgers. Chill in the refrigerator for 30 minutes.

5 Meanwhile, make the raita. Mix together the carrots, cucumber and Greek yogurt. Spoon into a small bowl and chill in the refrigerator until ready to serve.

6 Heat the remaining oil in a large frying pan. Fry the burgers, in batches if necessary, for 4–5 minutes on each side, or until lightly browned. Serve in the baps with tomato slices and lettuce. Accompany with the raita.

Ingredients SERVES 4

2^1/$_2$ tbsp sunflower oil
1 medium onion, peeled and very
  finely chopped
1 garlic clove, peeled and crushed
1 tsp curry paste
225 g/8 oz basmati rice
400 g can aduki beans,
  drained and rinsed
225 ml/8 fl oz vegetable stock
125 g/4 oz firm tofu, crumbled
1 tsp garam masala
2 tbsp freshly chopped coriander
salt and freshly ground black pepper

For the carrot raita:

2 large carrots, peeled and grated
^{1}/$_2$ cucumber, cut into tiny cubes
150 ml/^{1}/$_4$ pint Greek yogurt

To serve:

wholemeal baps
tomato slices
lettuce leaves

Nutritional details per 100 g energy 104 kcals/436 kj • protein 5 g • carbohydrate 15 g • fat 3 g • fibre 2.2 g • sugar 2.7 g • sodium 0.2 g

● cow's milk-free ✓ egg-free ● gluten-free ● wheat-free ✓ nut-free ✓ vegetarian ● vegan ✓ seafood-free

3

4

5

Braised Chicken with Aubergine

1 Heat a wok or large frying pan, add the oil and, when hot, add the chicken thighs and cook over a medium high heat for 5 minutes, or until browned all over. Transfer to a large plate and keep warm.

2 Add the aubergine to the wok and cook over a high heat for 5 minutes or until browned, turning occasionally. Add the garlic and ginger and stir-fry for 1 minute.

3 Return the chicken to the wok, pour in the stock and add the soy sauce and black beans. Bring to the boil, then simmer for 20 minutes, or until the chicken is tender. Add the spring onions after 10 minutes.

4 Blend the cornflour with 2 tablespoons of water. Stir into the wok and simmer until the sauce has thickened. Stir in the sesame oil, heat for 30 seconds, then remove from the heat. Garnish with spring onion tassels and serve immediately with noodles or rice.

Ingredients   SERVES 6

3 tbsp vegetable oil
12 chicken thighs
2 large aubergines, trimmed
  and cubed
4 garlic cloves, peeled and crushed
2 tsp freshly grated root ginger
900 ml/1$^{1}/_{2}$ pints vegetable stock
2 tbsp light soy sauce
2 tbsp Chinese preserved black beans
6 spring onions, trimmed and
  thinly sliced diagonally
1 tbsp cornflour
1 tbsp sesame oil
spring onion tassels, to garnish
freshly cooked noodles or rice,
  to serve

Nutritional details per 100 g   energy 80 kcals/337 kj • protein 7 g • carbohydrate 7 g • fat 3 g • fibre 1 g • sugar 0.2 g • sodium 0.2 g

✓ cow's milk-free   ✓ egg-free   ◔ gluten-free   ◔ wheat-free   ✓ nut-free   ◔ vegetarian   ◔ vegan   ✓ seafood-free

Broad Bean & Artichoke Risotto

1 Cook the beans in a saucepan of lightly salted boiling water for 4–5 minutes, or until just tender. Drain and plunge into cold water. Peel off the tough outer skins, if liked. Pat the artichokes dry on absorbent kitchen paper and cut each in half lengthways through the stem end. Cut each half into three wedges.

2 Heat the oil in a large saucepan and cook the artichokes for 4–5 minutes, turning occasionally, until they are lightly browned. Remove and reserve. Bring the wine and stock to the boil in a separate frying pan. Keep them barely simmering while making the risotto.

3 Melt the butter in a large frying pan, add the onion and cook for 5 minutes, until beginning to soften. Add the rice and cook for 1 minute, stirring. Pour in a ladleful of the hot wine and stock and simmer gently, stirring, until the stock is absorbed. Continue to add the stock in this way for 20–25 minutes, until the rice is just tender; the risotto should look creamy and soft.

4 Add the broad beans, artichokes and lemon rind and juice. Gently mix in, cover and leave to warm through for 1–2 minutes. Stir in the Parmesan cheese and season to taste with salt and pepper. Serve sprinkled with extra Parmesan cheese.

Ingredients   SERVES 4

275 g/10 oz frozen broad beans
400 g can artichoke hearts, drained
1 tbsp sunflower oil
150 ml/$1/_4$ pint dry white wine
900 ml/$1^1/_2$ pints vegetable stock
25 g/1 oz butter
1 onion, peeled and finely chopped
200 g/7 oz Arborio rice
juice and finely grated rind of
   1 lemon
50 g/2 oz Parmesan cheese, grated
salt and freshly ground black pepper
freshly grated Parmesan cheese,
   to serve

Nutritional details per 100 g energy 99 kcals/412 kj • protein 5 g • carbohydrate 11 g • fat 4 g • fibre 1.4 g • sugar 0.9 g • sodium 0.4 g

cow's milk-free   ✓ egg-free   gluten-free   wheat-free   ✓ nut-free   ✓ vegetarian   vegan   ✓ seafood-free

Brown Rice & Lentil Salad with Duck

1 Bring a large saucepan of water to the boil, sprinkle in the lentils, return to the boil, then simmer over a low heat for 30 minutes, or until tender; do not overcook. Drain and rinse under cold running water, then drain again and reserve.

2 Peel and finely chop the onion. Heat 2 tablespoons of the oil in a saucepan, add the onion and cook for 2 minutes until it begins to soften. Stir in the rice with the thyme and stock. Season to taste with salt and pepper and bring to the boil. Cover and simmer for 40 minutes, or until tender and the liquid is absorbed.

3 Heat the remaining oil in a large frying pan and add the mushrooms. Cook for 5 minutes until golden. Stir in the duck and garlic and cook for 2–3 minutes to heat through. Season well.

4 To make the dressing, whisk 2 tablespoons of red or white wine vinegar, 1 tablespoon of balsamic vinegar, 1 teaspoon of Dijon mustard and 1 teaspoon of clear honey in a large serving bowl, then gradually whisk in 75ml/3fl oz of extra virgin olive oil and 2 or 3 tablespoons of walnut oil. Add the lentils and the rice, then stir lightly together. Gently stir in the ham, blanched courgettes, spring onions and parsley. Season to taste and sprinkle with the walnuts. Serve topped with the duck and mushrooms.

Ingredients   SERVES 6

225 g/8 oz puy lentils, rinsed
4 tbsp olive oil; 1 medium onion
200 g/7 oz long–grain brown rice
$^1/_2$ tsp dried thyme
450 ml/$^3/_4$ pint chicken stock
salt and freshly ground black pepper
350 g/12 oz shiitake or portabella
   mushrooms, trimmed and sliced
375 g/13 oz cooked Chinese–style spicy
   duck or roasted duck, sliced into chunks
2 garlic cloves, peeled and finely chopped
125 g/4 oz cooked smoked ham, diced
2 small courgettes, trimmed, diced
   and blanched
6 spring onions, trimmed and thinly sliced
2 tbsp freshly chopped parsley
2 tbsp walnut halves, toasted and chopped

For the dressing:

2 tbsp red or white wine vinegar; 1 tbsp balsamic vinegar; 1 tsp Dijon mustard; 1 tsp clear honey; 75 ml/3 fl oz extra virgin olive oil; 2–3 tbsp walnut oil

Nutritional details per 100 g energy 117 kcals/724 kj • protein 10 g • carbohydrate 9 g • fat 12 g • fibre 1 g • sugar 1.2 g • sodium 0.3 g

✓ cow's milk-free   ✓ egg-free   gluten-free   wheat-free   nut-free   vegetarian   vegan   ✓ seafood-free

Cheese & Onion Oat Pie

1 Preheat the oven to 180°C/350°F/Gas Mark 4. Heat the oil and half the butter in a saucepan until melted. Add the onions and garlic and cook gently for 10 minutes, or until soft. Remove from the heat and tip into a large bowl.

2 Spread the oats out on a baking sheet and toast in the hot oven for 12 minutes. Leave to cool, then add to the onions with the cheese, eggs and parsley. Season to taste with salt and pepper and mix well.

3 Line the base of a 20.5 cm/8 inch round sandwich tin with greaseproof paper and oil well. Thinly slice the potato and arrange the slices on the base, overlapping them slightly.

4 Spoon the cheese and oat mixture on top of the potato, spreading evenly with the back of a spoon. Cover with foil and bake for 30 minutes.

5 Invert the pie onto a baking sheet so that the potatoes are on top. Carefully remove the tin and lining paper.

6 Preheat the grill to medium. Melt the remaining butter and brush carefully over the potato topping. Cook under the preheated grill for 5–6 minutes until the potatoes are lightly browned. Cut into wedges and serve.

Ingredients SERVES 4

1 tbsp sunflower oil, plus 1 tsp
25 g/1 oz butter
2 medium onions, peeled and sliced
1 garlic clove, peeled and crushed
150 g/5 oz porridge oats
125 g/4 oz mature Cheddar
  cheese, grated
2 medium eggs, lightly beaten
2 tbsp freshly chopped parsley
salt and freshly ground black pepper
275 g/10 oz baking potato, peeled

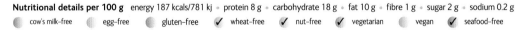

Nutritional details per 100 g energy 187 kcals/781 kj ● protein 8 g ● carbohydrate 18 g ● fat 10 g ● fibre 1 g ● sugar 2 g ● sodium 0.2 g

◐ cow's milk-free ◐ egg-free ◐ gluten-free ✓ wheat-free ✓ nut-free ✓ vegetarian ◐ vegan ✓ seafood-free

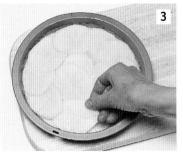

Creamy Puy Lentils

1 Put the lentils into a saucepan with plenty of cold water and bring to the boil.

2 Boil rapidly for 10 minutes, reduce the heat and simmer gently for a further 20 minutes until just tender. Drain well.

3 Meanwhile, prepare the dressing. Heat the oil in a frying pan over a medium heat.

4 Add the garlic and cook for about a minute until just beginning to brown. Add the lemon zest and juice.

5 Add the mustard and cook for a further 30 seconds.

6 Add the tarragon and crème fraîche and season to taste with salt and pepper.

7 Simmer and add the drained lentils, tomatoes and olives.

8 Transfer to a serving dish and sprinkle the chopped parsley on top.

9 Garnish the lentils with the tarragon sprigs and the lemon wedges and serve immediately.

Ingredients SERVES 4

225 g/8 oz puy lentils
1 tbsp olive oil
1 garlic clove, peeled and
   finely chopped
zest and juice of 1 lemon
1 tsp wholegrain mustard
1 tbsp freshly chopped tarragon
3 tbsp half-fat crème fraîche
salt and freshly ground black pepper
2 small tomatoes, deseeded
   and chopped
50 g/2 oz pitted black olives
1 tbsp freshly chopped parsley

To garnish:

sprigs of fresh tarragon
lemon wedges

Nutritional details per 100 g energy 84 kcals/353 kj • protein 4 g • carbohydrate 10 g • fat 4 g • fibre 2.2 g • sugar 1 g • sodium 0.3 g

cow's milk-free ✓ egg-free gluten-free wheat-free ✓ nut-free ✓ vegetarian vegan ✓ seafood-free

1

4

7

Mixed Grain Bread

1 Preheat the oven to 220°C/425°F/Gas Mark 7, 15 minutes before baking. Sift the white flour and salt into a large bowl. Stir in the Granary and rye flours, then rub in the butter until the mixture resembles breadcrumbs. Stir in the yeast, oats and seeds and make a well in the centre.

2 Stir the malt extract into the warm water until dissolved. Add the malt water to the dry ingredients. Mix to a soft dough.

3 Turn the dough out onto a lightly floured surface and knead for 10 minutes, until smooth and elastic.

4 Put in an oiled bowl, cover with clingfilm and leave to rise in a warm place for 1½ hours or until doubled in size.

5 Turn out and knead again for a minute or two to knock out the air. Shape into an oval loaf about 30.5 cm/12 inches long and place onto a well-oiled baking sheet. Cover with oiled clingfilm and leave to rise for 40 minutes, or until doubled in size.

6 Brush the loaf with beaten egg and bake in the preheated oven for 35–45 minutes, or until the bread is well risen, browned and sounds hollow when the base is tapped. Leave to cool on a wire rack, then serve.

Ingredients MAKES 1 LARGE LOAF

350 g/12 oz strong white flour
2 tsp salt
225 g/8 oz strong Granary flour
125 g/4 oz rye flour
25 g/1 oz butter, diced
2 tsp easy–blend dried yeast
25 g/1 oz rolled oats
2 tbsp sunflower seeds
1 tbsp malt extract
450 ml/³/₄ pint warm water
1 medium egg, beaten

Nutritional details per 100 g energy 338 kcals/1425 kj • protein 13 g • carbohydrate 64 g • fat 5 g • fibre 1.3 g • sugar 0.7 g • sodium 0.6 g

cow's milk-free   egg-free   gluten-free   wheat-free   ✓ nut-free   ✓ vegetarian   vegan   ✓ seafood-free

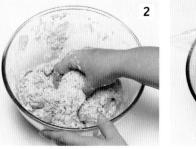
2

4

6

Mixed Grain Pilaf

1 Heat 1 tablespoon of the oil in a saucepan. Add the garlic and turmeric and cook for a few seconds. Stir in the rice and lentils. Add the stock, tomatoes and cinnamon. Season to taste with salt and pepper. Stir once and bring to the boil. Lower the heat, cover and simmer for 20 minutes, until most of the stock is absorbed and the rice and lentils are tender.

2 Stir in the beans, replace the lid and leave to stand for 2–3 minutes to allow the beans to heat through.

3 While the rice is cooking, heat the remaining oil and butter in a frying pan. Add the spring onions and cook for 4–5 minutes, until soft. Lightly beat the eggs with 2 tablespoons of the herbs, then season with salt and pepper.

4 Pour the egg mixture over the spring onions. Stir gently with a spatula over a low heat, drawing the mixture from the sides to the centre as the omelette sets. When almost set, stop stirring and cook for about 30 seconds until golden underneath.

5 Remove the omelette from the pan, roll up and slice into thin strips. Fluff the rice up with a fork and remove the cinnamon stick. Spoon onto serving plates, top with strips of omelette and the remaining chopped herbs. Garnish with sprigs of dill and serve.

Ingredients   SERVES 4

2 tbsp olive oil
1 garlic clove, peeled and crushed
$^1/_2$ tsp ground turmeric
125 g/4 oz mixed long–grain
    and wild rice
50 g/2 oz red lentils
300 ml/$^1/_2$ pint vegetable stock
200 g can chopped tomatoes
5 cm/2 inch piece cinnamon stick
salt and freshly ground black pepper
400 g can mixed beans, drained
    and rinsed
15 g/$^1/_2$ oz butter
1 bunch spring onions, trimmed
    and finely sliced
3 medium eggs
4 tbsp freshly chopped herbs,
    such as parsley and chervil
sprigs of fresh dill, to garnish

Nutritional details per 100 g   energy 98 kcals/412 kj • protein 5 g • carbohydrate 10 g • fat 4 g • fibre 2.5 g • sugar 2.3 g • sodium 0.3 g

cow's milk-free   egg-free   gluten-free   wheat-free   ✓ nut-free   ✓ vegetarian   vegan   ✓ seafood-free

Pasta & Pork Ragù

1   Heat the sunflower oil in a large frying pan. Add the sliced leek
    and cook, stirring frequently, for 5 minutes, or until softened.
    Add the pork and cook, stirring, for 4 minutes, or until sealed.

2   Add the crushed garlic and the paprika and cayenne peppers to
    the pan and stir until all the pork is lightly coated in the garlic
    and pepper mixture.

3   Pour in the wine and 450 ml/³/₄ pint of the vegetable stock.
    Add the borlotti beans and carrots and season to taste with
    salt and pepper. Bring the sauce to the boil, then lower the
    heat and simmer for 5 minutes.

4   Meanwhile, place the egg tagliatelle in a large saucepan of
    lightly salted, boiling water, then cover and simmer for
    5 minutes, or until the pasta is 'al dente'.

5   Drain the pasta, then add to the pork ragù and toss well. Adjust
    the seasoning, then tip into a warmed serving dish. Sprinkle
    with chopped parsley and serve with a little crème fraîche.

Ingredients   SERVES 4

1 tbsp sunflower oil
1 leek, trimmed and thinly sliced
225 g/8 oz pork fillet, diced
1 garlic clove, peeled and crushed
2 tsp paprika
¹/₄ tsp cayenne pepper
150 ml/¹/₄ pint white wine
600 ml/1 pint vegetable stock
400g can borlotti beans,
    drained and rinsed
2 carrots, peeled and diced
salt and freshly ground
    black pepper
225 g/8 oz fresh egg tagliatelle
1 tbsp freshly chopped parsley,
    to garnish
crème fraîche, to serve

Nutritional details per 100 g energy 117 kcals/489 kj • protein 9 g • carbohydrate 13 g • fat 3 g • fibre 1 g • sugar 1 g • sodium 0.1 g

● cow's milk-free   ● egg-free   ● gluten-free   ● wheat-free   ✓ nut-free   ● vegetarian   ● vegan   ✓ seafood-free

Pork in Peanut Sauce

1 Remove any fat or sinew from the pork fillet, cut into thin strips and reserve. Blend the soy sauce, vinegar, sugar, Chinese five-spice powder and garlic in a bowl and add the pork. Cover and leave to marinate in the refrigerator for at least 30 minutes.

2 Drain the pork, reserving any marinade. Heat the wok, then add the oil and, when hot, stir-fry the pork for 3–4 minutes, or until sealed.

3 Add the onion, carrots, celery and beans to the wok and stir-fry for 4–5 minutes, or until the meat is tender and the vegetables are softened.

4 Blend the reserved marinade, the peanut butter and 2 tablespoons of hot water together. When smooth, stir into the wok and cook for several minutes more until the sauce is thick and the pork is piping hot. Sprinkle with the chopped parsley and serve immediately with the basmati and wild rice and a green salad.

Ingredients SERVES 4

450 g/1 lb pork fillet
2 tbsp light soy sauce
1 tbsp vinegar
1 tsp sugar
1 tsp Chinese five-spice powder
2–4 garlic cloves, peeled and crushed
2 tbsp groundnut oil
1 large onion, peeled and
     finely sliced
125 g/4 oz carrots, peeled and
     cut into matchsticks
2 celery sticks, trimmed and sliced
125 g/4 oz French beans, trimmed
     and halved
3 tbsp smooth peanut butter
1 tbsp freshly chopped
     flat-leaf parsley

To serve:

freshly cooked basmati and wild rice
green salad

Nutritional details per 100 g energy 117 kcals/490 kj · protein 11 g · carbohydrate 8 g · fat 5 g · fibre 1 g · sugar 1.9 g · sodium 0.2 g

✓ cow's milk-free ✓ egg-free ◐ gluten-free ◐ wheat-free ◐ nut-free ◐ vegetarian ◐ vegan ✓ seafood-free

Pork with Black Bean Sauce

1   Using a sharp knife, trim the pork, discarding any fat or sinew and cut into bite-sized chunks. Place in a large shallow dish and spoon over the soy sauce. Turn to coat evenly, cover with clingfilm and leave to marinate for at least 30 minutes in the refrigerator. When ready to use, lift the pork from the marinade, shaking off as much marinade as possible, and pat dry with absorbent kitchen paper. Reserve the marinade.

2   Heat a wok, add the groundnut oil and, when hot, add the chopped garlic and ginger and stir-fry for 30 seconds. Add the carrot and the red and green peppers and stir-fry for 3–4 minutes or until just softened.

3   Add the pork to the wok and stir-fry for 5–7 minutes, or until browned all over and tender. Pour in the reserved marinade and black bean sauce. Bring to the boil, stirring constantly until well blended, then simmer for 1 minute until heated through thoroughly. Tip into a warmed serving dish or spoon on to individual plates. Garnish with snipped chives and serve immediately with steamed rice.

Ingredients   SERVES 4

700 g/1½ lb pork tenderloin
4 tbsp light soy sauce
2 tbsp groundnut oil
1 garlic clove, peeled and chopped
2.5 cm/1 inch piece fresh root
   ginger, peeled and cut into
   matchsticks
1 large carrot, peeled and sliced
1 red pepper, deseeded and sliced
1 green pepper, deseeded and sliced
160 g jar black bean sauce
snipped fresh chives, to garnish
freshly steamed rice, to serve

Nutritional details per 100 g energy 131 kcals/548 kj · protein 14 g · carbohydrate 9 g · fat 4 g · fibre 0.7 g · sugar 1.2 g · sodium 0.4 g

✓ cow's milk-free   ✓ egg-free   ◉ gluten-free   ◉ wheat-free   ◉ nut-free   ◉ vegetarian   ◉ vegan   ✓ seafood-free

1

2

3

Potato Skins

1 Preheat the oven to 200°C/400°F/Gas Mark 6. Scrub the potatoes, then prick a few times with a fork or skewer and place directly onto the top shelf of the oven. Bake in the preheated oven for at least 1 hour, or until tender. The potatoes are cooked when they yield gently to the pressure of your hand.

2 Set the potatoes aside until cool enough to handle, then cut in half and scoop the flesh into a bowl and reserve. Preheat the grill and line the grill rack with foil.

3 Mix together the oil and the paprika and use half to brush the outside of the potato skins. Place on the grill rack under the preheated hot grill and cook for 5 minutes, or until crisp, turning as necessary.

4 Heat the remaining paprika–flavoured oil and gently fry the pancetta until crisp. Add to the potato flesh along with the cream, Gorgonzola cheese and parsley. Halve the potato skins and fill with the Gorgonzola filling. Return to the oven for a further 15 minutes to heat through. Sprinkle with a little more paprika and serve immediately with mayonnaise, sweet chilli sauce and a green salad.

Ingredients   SERVES 4

4 large baking potatoes
2 tbsp olive oil
2 tsp paprika
125 g/4 oz pancetta,
    roughly chopped
6 tbsp double cream
125 g/4 oz Gorgonzola cheese
1 tbsp freshly chopped parsley

To serve:
mayonnaise
sweet chilli dipping sauce

Nutritional details per 100 g   energy 222 kcals/927 kj • protein 6 g • carbohydrate 20 g • fat 8 g • fibre 1.7 g • sugar 1.2 g • sodium 0.3 g

cow's milk-free   egg-free   gluten-free   wheat-free   ✓ nut-free   vegetarian   vegan   ✓ seafood-free

Red Lentil Kedgeree with Avocado & Tomatoes

1   Put the rice and lentils in a sieve and rinse under cold running water. Tip into a bowl, then pour over enough cold water to cover and leave to soak for 10 minutes.

2   Heat the butter and oil in a saucepan. Add the sliced onion and cook gently, stirring occasionally, for 10 minutes until softened. Stir in the cumin, cardamom pods and bay leaf and cook for a further minute, stirring all the time.

3   Drain the rice and lentils, rinse again and add to the onions in the saucepan. Stir in the vegetable stock and bring to the boil. Reduce the heat, cover the saucepan and simmer for about 15 minutes, or until the rice and lentils are tender.

4   Place the diced avocado in a bowl and toss with the lemon juice. Stir in the tomatoes and chopped coriander. Season to taste with salt and pepper.

5   Fluff up the rice with a fork, spoon into a warmed serving dish and spoon the avocado mixture on top. Garnish with lemon or lime slices and serve.

Ingredients   SERVES 4

150 g/5 oz basmati rice
150 g/5 oz red lentils
15 g/$^1/_2$ oz butter
1 tbsp sunflower oil
1 medium onion, peeled
   and chopped
1 tsp ground cumin
4 cardamom pods, bruised
1 bay leaf
450 ml/$^3/_4$ pint vegetable stock
1 ripe avocado, peeled,
   stoned and diced
1 tbsp lemon juice
4 plum tomatoes,
   peeled and diced
2 tbsp freshly chopped coriander
salt and freshly ground black pepper
lemon or lime slices, to garnish

Nutritional details per 100 g   energy 138 kcals/575 kj · protein 3 g · carbohydrate 13 g · fat 5 g · fibre 1.5 g · sugar 1.6 g · sodium 0.3 g

cow's milk-free   ✓ egg-free   gluten-free   wheat-free   ✓ nut-free   ✓ vegetarian   vegan   ✓ seafood-free

Roast Butternut Squash Risotto

1 Preheat the oven to 190°C/375°F/Gas Mark 5. Cut the squash in half, peel, then scoop out the seeds and discard. Cut the flesh into 2 cm/³/₄ inch cubes.

2 Pour the oil into a large roasting tin and heat in the preheated oven for 5 minutes. Add the butternut squash and garlic cloves. Turn in the oil to coat, then roast in the oven for about 25–30 minutes, or until golden brown and very tender, turning the vegetables halfway through cooking time.

3 Melt the butter in a large saucepan. Add the rice and stir over a high heat for a few seconds. Add the saffron and the wine and bubble fiercely until almost totally reduced, stirring frequently. At the same time heat the stock in a separate saucepan and keep at a steady simmer.

4 Reduce the heat under the rice to low. Add a ladleful of stock and simmer, stirring, until absorbed. Continue adding the stock in this way until the rice is tender. This will take about 20 minutes and it may not be necessary to add all the stock. Turn off the heat, stir in the herbs, Parmesan cheese and seasoning. Cover and leave to stand for 2–3 minutes. Remove the skins from the roasted garlic. Add to the risotto with the squash and mix gently. Garnish with sprigs of oregano and serve immediately with Parmesan.

Ingredients SERVES 4

1 medium butternut squash
2 tbsp olive oil
1 garlic bulb, cloves separated, but unpeeled
15 g/¹/₂ oz unsalted butter
275 g/10 oz Arborio rice
large pinch of saffron strands
150 ml/¹/₄ pint dry white wine
1 litre/1³/₄ pints vegetable stock
1 tbsp freshly chopped parsley
1 tbsp freshly chopped oregano
50 g/2 oz Parmesan cheese, finely grated
salt and freshly ground black pepper
sprigs of fresh oregano, to garnish
extra Parmesan cheese, to serve

Nutritional details per 100 g energy 88 kcals/368 kj • protein 3 g • carbohydrate 11 g • fat 4 g • fibre 0.8 g • sugar 0.1 g • sodium 0.2 g

cow's milk-free ✔ egg-free gluten-free wheat-free ✔ nut-free ✔ vegetarian vegan ✔ seafood-free

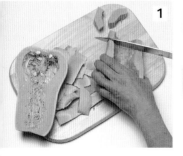

Oaty Fruit Puddings

1 Preheat the oven to 200°C/400°F/Gas Mark 6.

2 Lightly oil and line the bases of four individual pudding bowls or muffin tins with a small circle of greaseproof paper.

3 Mix together the oats, butter, nuts, honey and cinnamon in a small bowl.

4 Using a spoon, spread two thirds of the oaty mixture over the base and around the sides of the pudding bowls or muffin tins.

5 Toss together the pears and marmalade and spoon into the oaty cases.

6 Scatter over the remaining oaty mixture to cover the pears and marmalade.

7 Bake in the preheated oven for 15–20 minutes, until cooked and the tops of the puddings are golden and crisp.

8 Leave for 5 minutes before removing the pudding bowls or the muffin tins. Decorate with orange zest and serve hot with custard.

Ingredients   SERVES 4

125 g/4 oz rolled oats
50 g/2 oz butter, melted
2 tbsp chopped almonds
1 tbsp clear honey
pinch of ground cinnamon
2 pears, peeled, cored and
    finely chopped
1 tbsp marmalade
orange zest, to decorate
custard, to serve

Nutritional details per 100 g energy 138 kcals/581 kj • protein 5 g • carbohydrate 23 g • fat 3 g • fibre 1.2 g • sugar 12 g • sodium trace
◖ cow's milk-free   ◖ egg-free   ◖ gluten-free   ✓ wheat-free   ✓ nut-free   ✓ vegetarian   ◖ vegan   ✓ seafood-free

Sweet-stewed Dried Fruits

1 Place the fruits, apple juice, clear honey and brandy into a small saucepan.

2 Using a small, sharp knife or a zester, carefully remove the zest from the lemon and orange and place in the pan.

3 Squeeze the juice from the lemon and orange and add to the pan.

4 Bring the fruit mixture to the boil and simmer for about 1 minute. Remove the pan from the heat and allow the mixture to cool completely.

5 Transfer the mixture to a large bowl, cover with clingfilm and chill in the refrigerator overnight to allow the flavours to blend.

6 Spoon the stewed fruit into four shallow dessert dishes. Decorate with a large spoonful of crème fraîche and a few strips of the pared orange rind and serve.

Ingredients   SERVES 4

500 g/1 lb 2 oz packet mixed
    dried fruit salad
450 ml/³/₄ pint apple juice
2 tbsp clear honey
2 tbsp brandy
1 lemon
1 orange

To decorate:

crème fraîche
fine strips of pared orange rind

Nutritional details per 100 g   energy 139 kcals/529 kj • protein 1 g • carbohydrate 33 g • fat 1 g • fibre 2 g • sugar 26 g • sodium trace

cow's milk-free   ✓ egg-free   ✓ gluten-free   ✓ wheat-free   ✓ nut-free   ✓ vegetarian   vegan   ✓ seafood-free

Cancer-Fighting Food

Current research suggests that there is a link between cancer and the food that we eat. A poor diet may increase our chances of developing cancer. Conversely, certain foods have been singled out as being particularly good at fighting the disease. The following sumptuous recipes include as many of these 'superfoods' as possible.

Carrot & Ginger Soup

1 Preheat the oven to 180°C/350°F/Gas Mark 4. Roughly chop the bread. Dissolve the yeast extract in 2 tablespoons of warm water and mix with the bread.

2 Spread the bread cubes over a lightly oiled baking tray and bake for 20 minutes, turning halfway through. Remove from the oven and reserve.

3 Heat the oil in a large saucepan. Gently cook the onion and garlic for 3–4 minutes.

4 Stir in the ground ginger and cook for 1 minute to release the flavour.

5 Add the chopped carrots, then stir in the stock and the fresh ginger. Simmer gently for 15 minutes.

6 Remove from the heat and allow to cool a little. Blend until smooth, then season to taste with salt and pepper. Stir in the lemon juice. Top with the bread cubes, garnish with the chives and lemon zest and serve immediately.

Ingredients   SERVES 4

4 slices of bread, crusts removed
1 tsp yeast extract
2 tsp olive oil
1 onion, peeled and chopped
1 garlic clove, peeled
   and crushed
$^{1}/_{2}$ tsp ground ginger
450 g/1 lb carrots, peeled
   and chopped
1 litre/1$^{3}/_{4}$ pints vegetable stock
2.5 cm/1 inch piece root ginger,
   peeled and finely grated
salt and freshly ground
   black pepper
1 tbsp lemon juice

To garnish:

chives
lemon zest

Nutritional details per 100 g   energy 75 kcals/314 kj • protein 3 g • carbohydrate 13 g • fat 2 g • fibre 2 g • sugar 4.3 g • sodium 0.5 g

✓ cow's milk-free   ✓ egg-free   ◐ gluten-free   ◐ wheat-free   ✓ nut-free   ✓ vegetarian   ✓ vegan   ✓ seafood-free

Hot Herby Mushrooms

1 Preheat the oven to 180°C/350°F/Gas Mark 4. With a rolling pin, roll each piece of bread out as thinly as possible.

2 Press each piece of bread into a 10 cm/4 inch tartlet tin. Push each piece down firmly , then bake in the preheated oven for 20 minutes.

3 Place the mushrooms in a frying pan with the garlic, mustard and vegetable stock and stir-fry over a moderate heat until the mushrooms are tender and the liquid is reduced by half.

4 Carefully remove the mushrooms from the frying pan with a slotted spoon and transfer to a heat-resistant dish. Cover with foil and place in the bottom of the oven to keep the mushrooms warm.

5 Boil the remaining pan juices until reduced to a thick sauce. Season with salt and pepper.

6 Stir the parsley and the chives into the mushroom mixture.

7 Place one bread tartlet case on each plate and divide the mushroom mixture between them.

8 Spoon over the pan juices, garnish with the chives and serve immediately with mixed salad leaves.

Ingredients   SERVES 4

4 thin slices of white bread,
  crusts removed
125 g/4 oz chestnut mushrooms,
  wiped and sliced
125 g/4 oz oyster
  mushrooms, wiped
1 garlic clove, peeled and crushed
1 tsp Dijon mustard
300 ml/¹/₂ pint vegetable stock
salt and freshly ground
  black pepper
1 tbsp freshly chopped parsley
1 tbsp freshly snipped chives,
  plus extra to garnish
mixed salad leaves, to serve

Nutritional details per 100 g energy 81 kcals/342 kj • protein 4 g • carbohydrate 15 g • fat 1 g • fibre 0.7 g • sugar 1.8 g • sodium 0.5 g

✓ cow's milk-free   ✓ egg-free   ◉ gluten-free   ◉ wheat-free   ✓ nut-free   ✓ vegetarian   ✓ vegan   ✓ seafood-free

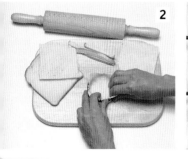

Citrus-grilled Plaice

1 Heat the oil in a large frying pan, then sauté the onion, pepper and rice for 2 minutes.

2 Add the orange and lemon juice and bring to the boil. Reduce the heat, add half the stock and simmer for 15–20 minutes, or until the rice is tender, adding the remaining stock as necessary.

3 Preheat the grill. Finely spray the base of the grill pan with oil. Place the fish fillets in the base and reserve.

4 Finely grate the orange and lemon rind. Squeeze the juice from half of each fruit.

5 Melt the butter or low-fat spread in a small saucepan. Add the grated rind, juice and half of the tarragon and use to baste the plaice fillets.

6 Cook one side only of the fish under the preheated grill at a medium heat for 4–6 minutes, basting continuously.

7 Once the rice is cooked, stir in the remaining tarragon and season to taste with salt and pepper. Garnish the fish with the lemon wedges and serve immediately with the rice.

Ingredients   SERVES 4

1 tsp sunflower oil
1 onion, peeled and chopped
1 orange pepper, deseeded
    and chopped
175 g/6 oz long-grain rice
150 ml/¹/₄ pint orange juice
2 tbsp lemon juice
225 ml/8 fl oz vegetable stock
spray of oil
4 x 175 g/6 oz plaice fillets, skinned
1 orange
1 lemon
25 g/1 oz half-fat butter
    or low-fat spread
2 tbsp freshly chopped tarragon
salt and freshly ground
    black pepper
lemon wedges, to garnish

Nutritional details per 100 g energy 74 kcals/312 kj • protein 8 g • carbohydrate 8 g • fat 1 g • fibre 0.4 g • sugar 1.4 g • sodium 0.2 g
  cow's milk-free   ✓ egg-free   gluten-free   wheat-free   ✓ nut-free   vegetarian   vegan   seafood-free

Indonesian Salad with Peanut Dressing

1 Cook the potatoes in a saucepan of boiling salted water for 15–20 minutes until tender. Remove with a slotted spoon and slice thickly into a large bowl. Keep the saucepan of water boiling.

2 Add the carrot, French beans and cauliflower to the water, return to the boil and cook for 2 minutes, or until just tender. Drain and refresh under cold running water, then drain well. Add to the potatoes with the cucumber and bean sprouts.

3 To make the dressing, gently heat the sesame oil in a small saucepan. Add the garlic and chilli and cook for a few seconds, then remove from the heat. Stir in the peanut butter.

4 Stir in the stock, a little at a time. Add the remaining ingredients and mix together to make a thick, creamy dressing.

5 Divide the vegetables between four plates and arrange the eggs on top. Drizzle the dressing over the salad and serve immediately.

Ingredients   SERVES 4

225 g/8 oz new potatoes, scrubbed
1 large carrot, peeled and cut
    into matchsticks
125 g/4 oz French beans, trimmed
225 g/8 oz tiny cauliflower florets
125 g/4 oz cucumber, cut
    into matchsticks
75 g/3 oz fresh bean sprouts
3 medium eggs, hard–boiled
    and quartered

For the peanut dressing:

2 tbsp sesame oil
1 garlic clove, peeled and crushed
1 red chilli, deseeded and
    finely chopped
150 g/5 oz crunchy peanut butter
6 tbsp hot vegetable stock
2 tsp soft light brown sugar
2 tsp dark soy sauce
1 tbsp lime juice

Nutritional details per 100 g energy 134 kcals/560 kj • protein 6 g • carbohydrate 8 g • fat 9 g • fibre 1.3 g • sugar 2.1 g • sodium 0.2 g

✓ cow's milk–free   egg–free   gluten–free   wheat–free   nut–free   ✓ vegetarian   vegan   ✓ seafood–free

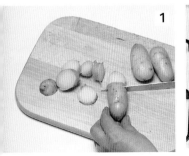

Fusilli Pasta with Spicy Tomato Salsa

1 Place the tomatoes in a bowl and cover with boiling water. Allow to stand until the skins start to peel away.

2 Remove the skins from the tomatoes, divide each tomato in four and remove all the seeds. Chop the flesh into small cubes and put in a small pan. Add the lemon and lime juice and the grated lime rind and stir well.

3 Add the chopped shallots and garlic. Remove the seeds carefully from the chillies, chop finely and add to the pan.

4 Bring to the boil and simmer gently for 5–10 minutes until the salsa has thickened slightly.

5 Reserve the salsa to allow the flavours to develop while the pasta is cooking.

6 Bring a large pan of water to the boil and add the pasta. Simmer gently for 3–4 minutes or until the pasta is just tender.

7 Drain the pasta and rinse in boiling water. Mix with the salsa and divide onto serving plates. Top each with a small spoonful of crème fraîche. Garnish with the chopped basil and oregano and serve immediately.

Ingredients
SERVES 4

6 large ripe tomatoes
2 tbsp lemon juice
2 tbsp lime juice
grated rind of 1 lime
2 shallots, peeled and
    finely chopped
2 garlic cloves, peeled and
    finely chopped
1–2 red chillies
1–2 green chillies
450 g/1 lb fresh fusilli pasta
4 tbsp half-fat crème fraîche
2 tbsp freshly chopped basil
sprig of oregano, to garnish

Nutritional details per 100 g   energy 59 kcals/252 kj • protein 3 g • carbohydrate 12 g • fat 0.7 g • fibre 0.6 g • sugar 0.3 g • sodium trace

cow's milk-free   ✓ egg-free   gluten-free   wheat-free   ✓ nut-free   ✓ vegetarian   vegan   ✓ seafood-free

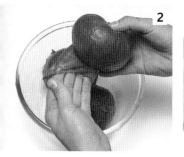

2

3

6

Teriyaki Turkey with Oriental Vegetables

1 Halve, deseed and thinly slice the chilli. Put into a small bowl with the garlic, ginger, soy sauce and sunflower oil.

2 Cut the turkey into thin strips. Add to the mixture and stir until well coated. Cover with clingfilm and marinate in the refrigerator for at least 30 minutes.

3 Heat a wok or large frying pan. Add 2 teaspoons of the sesame oil. When hot, remove the turkey from the marinade. Stir–fry for 2–3 minutes until browned and cooked. Remove from the pan and reserve. Heat the remaining 1 teaspoon of oil in the wok. Add the sesame seeds and stir–fry for a few seconds until they start to change colour.

4 Add the carrots, leek and broccoli and stir–fry for 2–3 minutes.

5 Blend the cornflour with 1 tablespoon of cold water to make a paste. Stir in the sherry and marinade. Add to the wok with the mangetout and cook for 1 minute, stirring, until thickened.

6 Return the turkey to the pan and continue cooking for 1–2 minutes or until the turkey is hot, the vegetables are tender and the sauce is bubbling. Serve immediately with the egg noodles. Sprinkle with the sesame seeds.

Ingredients SERVES 4

1 red chilli
1 garlic clove, peeled and crushed
2.5 cm/1 inch piece root ginger, peeled and grated
3 tbsp dark soy sauce
1 tsp sunflower oil
350 g/12 oz skinless, boneless turkey breast
1 tbsp sesame oil
1 tbsp sesame seeds
2 carrots, peeled and cut into matchsticks
1 leek, trimmed and shredded
125 g/4 oz broccoli, cut into tiny florets
1 tsp cornflour
3 tbsp dry sherry
125 g/4 oz mangetout, cut into thin strips

To serve:

freshly cooked egg noodles
sprinkling of sesame seeds

Nutritional details per 100 g energy 79 kcals/335 kj • protein 9 g • carbohydrate 7 g • fat 2 g • fibre 1 g • sugar 1.5 g • sodium 0.2 g

✓ cow's milk-free   egg-free   gluten-free   wheat-free   ✓ nut-free   vegetarian   vegan   ✓ seafood-free

Beef Fajitas with Avocado Sauce

1 Heat the wok, add the oil, then stir–fry the beef for 3–4 minutes. Add the garlic and spices and continue to cook for a further 2 minutes. Stir the tomatoes into the wok, bring to the boil, cover and simmer gently for 5 minutes.

2 Meanwhile, blend the kidney beans in a food processor until slightly broken up, then add to the wok. Continue to cook for a further 5 minutes, adding 2–3 tablespoons of water. The mixture should be thick and fairly dry. Stir in the chopped coriander.

3 Mix the chopped avocado, shallot, tomato, chilli and lemon juice together. Spoon into a serving dish and reserve.

4 When ready to serve, warm the tortillas and spread with a little soured cream. Place a spoonful of the beef mixture on top, followed by a spoonful of the avocado sauce, then roll up. Repeat until all the mixture is used up. Serve immediately with a green salad.

Ingredients   SERVES 3-6

2 tbsp sunflower oil
450 g/1 lb beef fillet or rump
    steak, trimmed and cut into
    thin strips
2 garlic cloves, peeled
    and crushed
1 tsp ground cumin
$1/4$ tsp cayenne pepper
1 tbsp paprika
230 g can chopped tomatoes
215 g can red kidney beans, drained
1 tbsp freshly chopped coriander
1 avocado, peeled, pitted
    and chopped
1 shallot, peeled and chopped
1 large tomato, skinned,
    deseeded and chopped
1 red chilli, diced
1 tbsp lemon juice
6 large flour tortilla pancakes
3–4 tbsp soured cream
green salad, to serve

Nutritional details per 100 g   energy 177 kcals/740 kj • protein 11 g • carbohydrate 16 g • fat 8 g • fibre 1.2 g • sugar 1.4 g • sodium 0.2 g

cow's milk-free   ✓ egg-free   gluten-free   wheat-free   ✓ nut-free   vegetarian   vegan   ✓ seafood-free

Lamb Meatballs with Savoy Cabbage

1 Place the lamb mince in a large bowl with the parsley, ginger, light soy sauce and egg yolk and mix together. Divide the mixture into walnut–sized pieces and, using your hands, roll into balls. Place on a baking sheet, cover with clingfilm and chill in the refrigerator for at least 30 minutes.

2 Meanwhile, blend together the dark soy sauce, sherry and cornflour with 2 tablespoons of water in a small bowl until smooth. Reserve.

3 Heat a wok, add the oil and when hot, add the meatballs and cook for 5–8 minutes, or until browned all over, turning occasionally. Using a slotted spoon, transfer the meatballs to a large plate and keep warm.

4 Add the garlic, spring onions, Savoy cabbage and the Chinese leaves to the wok and stir–fry for 3 minutes. Pour over the reserved soy sauce mixture, bring to the boil, then simmer for 30 seconds or until thickened. Return the meatballs to the wok and mix in. Garnish with chopped red chilli and serve immediately.

Ingredients SERVES 4

450 g/1 lb fresh lamb mince
1 tbsp freshly chopped parsley
1 tbsp freshly grated root ginger
1 tbsp light soy sauce
1 medium egg yolk
4 tbsp dark soy sauce
2 tbsp dry sherry
1 tbsp cornflour
3 tbsp vegetable oil
2 garlic cloves, peeled and chopped
1 bunch spring onions, trimmed
   and shredded
$^1/_2$ Savoy cabbage, trimmed
   and shredded
$^1/_2$ head Chinese leaves, trimmed
   and shredded
freshly chopped red chilli,
   to garnish

Nutritional details per 100 g energy 105 kcals/437 kj • protein 8 g • carbohydrate 5 g • fat 6 g • fibre trace • sugar 0.4 g • sodium 0.3 g

✓ cow's milk-free   egg-free   gluten-free   wheat-free   ✓ nut-free   vegetarian   vegan   ✓ seafood-free

1

3

4

Pasta Shells with Broccoli & Capers

1 Bring a large pan of lightly salted water to a rolling boil. Add the pasta shells, return to the boil and cook for 2 minutes. Add the broccoli to the pan. Return to the boil and continue cooking for 8–10 minutes, or until the conchiglie is 'al dente'.

2 Meanwhile, heat the olive oil in a large frying pan, add the onion and cook for 5 minutes, or until softened, stirring frequently. Stir in the capers and chilli flakes, if using, and cook for a further 2 minutes.

3 Drain the pasta and broccoli and add to the frying pan. Toss the ingredients to mix thoroughly. Sprinkle over the cheeses, then stir until the cheeses have just melted. Season to taste with salt and pepper, then tip into a warmed serving dish. Garnish with chopped parsley and serve immediately with extra Parmesan cheese.

Ingredients　　　　SERVES 4

400 g/14 oz conchiglie (shells)

450 g/1 lb broccoli florets, cut into
　small pieces

5 tbsp olive oil

1 large onion, peeled and
　finely chopped

4 tbsp capers in brine, rinsed
　and drained

$^1/_2$ tsp dried chilli flakes (optional)

75 g/3 oz freshly grated
　Parmesan cheese, plus
　extra to serve

25 g/1 oz pecorino cheese, grated

salt and freshly ground black pepper

2 tbsp freshly chopped flat–leaf
　parsley, to garnish

Nutritional details per 100 g　energy 136 kcals/569 kj · protein 6 g · carbohydrate 12 g · fat 7 g · fibre 1.7 g · sugar 1.6 g · sodium 0.2 g

cow's milk-free　　egg-free　　gluten-free　　wheat-free　　✓ nut-free　　✓ vegetarian　　vegan　　✓ seafood-free

Stir-fried Greens

1   Separate the Chinese leaves and pak choi and wash well.
Cut into 2.5 cm/1 inch strips. Separate the broccoli into small
florets. Heat a wok or large frying pan, add the sesame seeds
and stir-fry for 30 seconds or until browned.

2   Add the oil to the wok and when hot, add the ginger, garlic
and chillies and stir-fry for 30 seconds. Add the broccoli
and stir-fry for 1 minute. Add the Chinese leaves and pak
choi and stir-fry for a further 1 minute.

3   Pour the vegetable stock and Chinese rice wine into the wok
with the soy and black bean sauces. Season to taste with
pepper and add the sugar. Reduce the heat and simmer for
6–8 minutes, or until the vegetables are tender but still firm to
the bite. Tip into a warmed serving dish, removing the chillies if
preferred. Drizzle with the sesame oil and serve immediately.

Ingredients   SERVES 4

450 g/1 lb Chinese leaves
225 g/8 oz pak choi
225 g/8 oz broccoli florets
1 tbsp sesame seeds
1 tbsp groundnut oil
1 tbsp fresh root ginger, peeled
   and finely chopped
3 garlic cloves, peeled and
   finely chopped
2 red chillies, deseeded and
   split in half
50 ml/2 fl oz vegetable stock
2 tbsp Chinese rice wine
1 tbsp dark soy sauce
1 tsp light soy sauce
2 tsp black bean sauce
freshly ground black pepper
2 tsp sugar
1 tsp sesame oil

Nutritional details per 100 g   energy 38 kcals/158 kj • protein 2 g • carbohydrate 5 g • fat 2 g • fibre trace • sugar 1 g • sodium 0.2 g

✔ cow's milk-free   ✔ egg-free   ◐ gluten-free   ◐ wheat-free   ◐ nut-free   ✔ vegetarian   ✔ vegan   ✔ seafood-free

1

2

3

Rice & Papaya Salad

1 Rinse and drain the rice and pour into a saucepan. Add 450 ml/³/₄ pint of boiling salted water and the cinnamon stick. Bring to the boil, reduce to a very low heat, then cover and cook without stirring for 15–18 minutes, or until all the liquid is absorbed. The rice should be light and fluffy and have steam holes on the surface. Remove the cinnamon stick and stir in the rind from 1 lime.

2 To make the dressing, place the bird's-eye chilli, remaining rind and lime and lemon juice, fish sauce and sugar in a food processor and mix until blended. Alternatively, place all the ingredients in a screw-top jar and shake until mixed. Pour half the dressing over the hot rice and toss until the rice glistens.

3 Slice the papaya and mango into thin slices, then place in a bowl. Add the chopped green chilli, coriander and mint. Place the chicken onto a chopping board, then remove and discard any skin or sinews. Cut into fine shreds and add to the bowl with the chopped peanuts.

4 Add the remaining dressing to the chicken mixture and stir until all the ingredients are lightly coated. Spoon the rice onto a platter, pile the chicken mixture on top and serve with warm strips of pitta bread.

Ingredients   SERVES 4

175 g/6 oz easy-cook basmati rice
1 cinnamon stick, bruised
1 bird's-eye chilli, deseeded
    and finely chopped
rind and juice of 2 limes
rind and juice of 2 lemons
2 tbsp Thai fish sauce
1 tbsp soft light brown sugar
1 papaya, peeled and seeds removed
1 mango, peeled and stone removed
1 green chilli, deseeded and
    finely chopped
2 tbsp freshly chopped coriander
1 tbsp freshly chopped mint
250 g/9 oz cooked chicken
50 g/2 oz roasted peanuts, chopped
strips of pitta bread, to serve

Nutritional details per 100 g energy 108 kcals/455 kj ▪ protein 8 g ▪ carbohydrate 17 g ▪ fat 2 g ▪ fibre 0.4 g ▪ sugar 1.7 g ▪ sodium trace
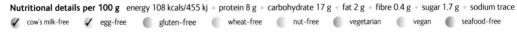
✓ cow's milk-free   ✓ egg-free   ◖ gluten-free   ◖ wheat-free   ◖ nut-free   ◖ vegetarian   ◖ vegan   ◖ seafood-free

1

3

3

Thai Noodles & Vegetables with Tofu

1 Drain the tofu well and cut into cubes. Put into a shallow dish with the soy sauce and lime rind. Stir well to coat and leave to marinate for 30 minutes.

2 Meanwhile, put the lemon grass and chilli on a chopping board and bruise with the side of a large knife, ensuring the blade is pointing away from you. Put the vegetable stock in a large saucepan and add the lemon grass, chilli, ginger, garlic, and coriander. Bring to the boil, cover and simmer gently for 20 minutes.

3 Strain the stock into a clean pan. Return to the boil and add the noodles, tofu and its marinade and the mushrooms. Simmer gently for 4 minutes.

4 Add the carrots, mangetout, pak choi and coriander and simmer for a further 3–4 minutes until the vegetables are just tender. Season to taste with salt and pepper. Garnish with coriander sprigs and serve immediately.

Ingredients
SERVES 4

225 g/8 oz firm tofu
2 tbsp soy sauce
rind of 1 lime, grated
2 lemon grass stalks
1 red chilli
1 litre/1³/₄ pints vegetable stock
2 slices fresh root ginger, peeled
2 garlic cloves, peeled
2 sprigs of fresh coriander
175 g/6 oz dried thread egg noodles
125 g/4 oz shiitake or button
    mushrooms, sliced if large
2 carrots, peeled and cut
    into matchsticks
125 g/4 oz mangetout
125 g/4 oz pak choi or other
    Chinese leaf
1 tbsp freshly chopped coriander
salt and freshly ground black pepper
coriander sprigs, to garnish

Nutritional details per 100 g energy 52 kcals/217 kj • protein 4 g • carbohydrate 7 g • fat 1 g • fibre 0.4 g • sugar 0.7 g • sodium 0.5 g

✓ cow's milk-free   egg-free   gluten-free   wheat-free   ✓ nut-free   ✓ vegetarian   vegan   ✓ seafood-free

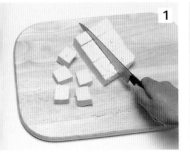
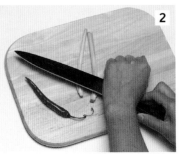

Vegetables Braised in Olive Oil & Lemon

1 Put the pared lemon rind and juice into a large saucepan. Add the olive oil, bay leaf, thyme and the water. Bring to the boil. Add the spring onions and mushrooms. Top with the broccoli and cauliflower, trying to add them so that the stalks are submerged in the water and the tops are just above it. Cover and simmer for 3 minutes.

2 Scatter the courgettes on top, so that they are steamed rather than boiled. Cook, covered, for a further 3–4 minutes, until all the vegetables are tender. Using a slotted spoon, transfer the vegetables from the liquid into a warmed serving dish. Increase the heat and boil rapidly for 3–4 minutes, or until the liquid is reduced to about 8 tablespoons. Remove the lemon rind, bay leaf and thyme sprig and discard.

3 Stir the chives into the reduced liquid, season to taste with salt and pepper and pour over the vegetables. Sprinkle with lemon zest and serve immediately.

Ingredients   SERVES 4

juice and small strip of pared rind
  of $1/2$ lemon
4 tbsp olive oil
1 bay leaf
large sprig of thyme
150 ml/$1/4$ pint water
4 spring onions, trimmed and
  finely chopped
175 g/6 oz baby button mushrooms
175 g/6 oz broccoli, cut into
  small florets
175 g/6 oz cauliflower, cut into
  small florets
1 medium courgette, sliced on
  the diagonal
2 tbsp freshly snipped chives
salt and freshly ground
  black pepper
lemon zest, to garnish

Nutritional details per 100 g energy 72 kcals/297 kj • protein 2 g • carbohydrate 2 g • fat 6 g • fibre 1.4 g • sugar 1.1 g • sodium trace
  ✓ cow's milk-free   ✓ egg-free   ✓ gluten-free   ✓ wheat-free   ✓ nut-free   ✓ vegetarian   ✓ vegan   ✓ seafood-free

Wild Garlic Mushrooms with Pizza Breadsticks

1 Preheat the oven to 240°C/475°F/Gas Mark 9, 15 minutes before baking. Place the dried yeast in the warm water for 10 minutes. Place the flour in a large bowl and gradually blend in the olive oil, salt and the dissolved yeast.

2 Knead on a lightly floured surface to form a smooth and pliable dough. Cover with clingfilm and leave in a warm place for 15 minutes to allow the dough to rise, then roll out again and cut into sticks of equal length. Cover and leave to rise again for 10 minutes. Brush with the olive oil, sprinkle with salt and bake in the preheated oven for 10 minutes.

3 Pour 3 tablespoons of the oil into a frying pan and add the crushed garlic. Cook over a very low heat, stirring well for 3–4 minutes to flavour the oil.

4 Cut the wild mushrooms into bite–sized slices if very large, then add to the pan. Season well with salt and pepper and cook very gently for 6–8 minutes, or until tender.

5 Whisk the fresh herbs, the remaining olive oil and lemon juice together. Pour over the mushrooms and heat through. Season to taste and place on individual serving dishes. Serve with the pizza breadsticks.

Ingredients SERVES 6

For the breadsticks:
7 g/¼ oz dried yeast
250 ml/8 fl oz warm water
400 g/14 oz strong, plain flour
2 tbsp olive oil
1 tsp salt

For the mushrooms:
9 tbsp olive oil
4 garlic cloves, peeled
    and crushed
450 g/1 lb mixed wild mushrooms,
    wiped and dried
salt and freshly ground
    black pepper
1 tbsp freshly chopped parsley
1 tbsp freshly chopped basil
1 tsp fresh oregano leaves
juice of 1 lemon

Nutritional details per 100 g energy 249 kcals/1045 kj • protein 6 g • carbohydrate 32 g • fat 12 g • fibre 1.3 g • sugar 0.6 g • sodium 0.2 g

✓ cow's milk-free ✓ egg-free ◐ gluten–free ◐ wheat–free ✓ nut–free ✓ vegetarian ✓ vegan ✓ seafood–free

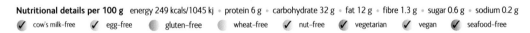

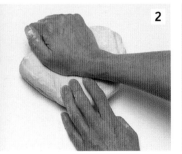

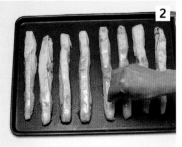

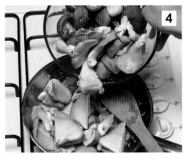

Creamy Puddings with Mixed Berry Compote

1   Set the freezer to rapid freeze. Whip the cream until soft peaks form. Fold in the ricotta cheese and half the sugar.

2   Place the chocolate in a bowl set over a saucepan of simmering water. Stir until melted.

3   Remove from the heat and leave to cool, stirring occasionally. Stir into the cheese mixture until well blended.

4   Spoon the mixture into six individual pudding moulds and level the surface of each pudding with the back of a spoon. Place in the freezer and freeze for 4 hours.

5   Place the fruits and the remaining sugar in a pan and heat gently, stirring occasionally until the sugar has dissolved and the juices are just beginning to run. Stir in the Cointreau to taste.

6   Dip the pudding moulds in hot water for 30 seconds and invert onto six serving plates. Spoon the fruit compote over the puddings and serve immediately. Remember to return the freezer to its normal setting.

Ingredients   SERVES 6

300 ml/$^{1}/_{2}$ pint half–fat double cream
1 x 250 g carton ricotta cheese
50 g/2 oz caster sugar
125 g/4 oz white chocolate, broken into pieces
350 g/12 oz mixed summer fruits such as strawberries, blueberries and raspberries
2 tbsp Cointreau

Nutritional details per 100 g   energy 232 kcals/968 kj • protein 5 g • carbohydrate 18 g • fat 16 g • fibre 0.4 g • sugar 15 g • sodium trace

  cow's milk-free   ✔ egg-free   ✔ gluten-free   ✔ wheat-free   ✔ nut-free   ✔ vegetarian   vegan   ✔ seafood-free

Grape & Almond Layer

1 Mix together the fromage frais and yogurt in a bowl and lightly fold in the sifted icing sugar and crème de cassis with a large metal spoon or rubber spatula until lightly blended.

2 Using a small knife, remove the seeds from the grapes if necessary. Rinse lightly and pat dry on absorbent kitchen paper.

3 Place the deseeded grapes in a bowl and stir in any juice from the grapes from deseeding.

4 Place the Amaretti biscuits in a polythene bag and crush roughly with a rolling pin. Alternatively, use a food processor.

5 Cut the passion fruit in half, scoop out the seeds with a teaspoon and reserve.

6 Divide the yogurt mixture between four tall glasses, then layer alternately with grapes, crushed biscuits and most of the passion fruit seeds. Top with the yogurt mixture and the remaining passion fruit seeds. Chill for 1 hour and decorate with extra grapes. Lightly dust with icing sugar and serve.

Ingredients   SERVES 4

300 ml/¹/₂ pint low-fat
   fromage frais
300 ml/¹/₂ pint half-fat
   Greek set yogurt
3 tbsp icing sugar, sifted
2 tbsp crème de cassis
450 g/1 lb red grapes
175 g/6 oz Amaretti biscuits
2 ripe passion fruit

To decorate:

icing sugar
extra grapes (optional)

Nutritional details per 100 g energy 97 kcals/409 kj • protein 3 g • carbohydrate 18 g • fat 2 g • fibre 0.4 g • sugar 10.7 g • sodium trace

● cow's milk-free   ✔ egg-free   ● gluten-free   ● wheat-free   ● nut-free   ✔ vegetarian   ● vegan   ✔ seafood-free

Orange Freeze

1 Set the freezer to rapid freeze. Using a sharp knife carefully cut the lid off each orange. Scoop out the flesh from the orange, discarding any pips and thick pith. Place the shells and lids in the freezer and chop any remaining orange flesh. Whisk together the orange juice, orange flesh and vanilla ice cream, until well blended.

2 Cover and freeze for about 2 hours, occasionally breaking up the ice crystals with a fork or a whisk. Stir the mixture from around the edge of the container into the centre, then level and return to the freezer. Do this 2–3 times then leave until almost frozen solid.

3 Place a large scoop of the ice cream mixture into the frozen shells. Add another scoop on top, so that there is plenty outside of the orange shell and return to the freezer for 1 hour. Arrange the lids on top and freeze for a further 2 hours, until the filled orange shell is completely frozen solid.

4 Meanwhile, using a nylon sieve, press the raspberries into a bowl using the back of a wooden spoon and mix together with the icing sugar. Spoon the raspberry coulis onto four serving plates and place an orange at the centre of each. Dust with icing sugar and serve decorated with the redcurrants. Remember to return the freezer to its normal setting.

Ingredients   SERVES 4

4 large oranges
about 300 ml/$\frac{1}{2}$ pint low–fat
    vanilla ice cream
225 g/8 oz raspberries
75 g/3 oz icing sugar, sifted
redcurrant sprigs, to decorate

Nutritional details per 100 g   energy 72 kcals/303 kj • protein 1 g • carbohydrate 14 g • fat 1 g • fibre 1.5 g • sugar 8.5 g • sodium trace
cow's milk–free ● egg–free ● ✓ gluten–free ✓ wheat–free ✓ nut–free ✓ vegetarian ● vegan ● ✓ seafood–free

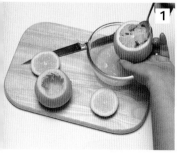

Combating High Blood Pressure

High blood pressure has been linked to life-endangering health problems such as strokes, heart attacks and blood clots. This section provides recipes that are low in salt and fat (which can increase the chance of high blood pressure) and high in fibre and essential oils (which can help to prevent it). These healthier meals still retain their taste and are easy to prepare.

Citrus Monkfish Kebabs

1 Preheat the grill and line the grill rack with foil. Mix all the marinade ingredients together in a small bowl and reserve.

2 Using a sharp knife, cut down both sides of the monkfish tail. Remove the bone and discard. Cut away and discard any skin, then cut the monkfish into bite–sized cubes.

3 Peel the prawns, leaving the tails intact and remove the thin black vein that runs down the back of each prawn. Place the fish and prawns in a shallow dish.

4 Pour the marinade over the fish and prawns. Cover lightly and leave to marinate in the refrigerator for 30 minutes. Spoon the marinade over the fish and prawns occasionally during this time. Soak the skewers in cold water for 30 minutes, then drain.

5 Thread the cubes of fish, prawns and courgettes onto the drained skewers. Arrange on the grill rack then place under the preheated grill and cook for 5–7 minutes, or until cooked thoroughly and the prawns have turned pink. Occasionally brush with the remaining marinade and turn the kebabs during cooking.

6 Mix 2 tablespoons of marinade with the crème fraîche and serve as a dip with the kebabs.

Ingredients   SERVES 4

For the marinade:

1 tbsp sunflower oil
juice and finely grated rind of 1 lime
1 tbsp lemon juice
1 sprig of freshly chopped rosemary
1 tbsp wholegrain mustard
1 garlic clove, peeled and crushed
freshly ground black pepper

For the kebabs:

450 g/1 lb monkfish tail
8 raw tiger prawns
1 small green courgette, trimmed
    and sliced
4 tbsp of half–fat crème fraîche

Nutritional details per 100 g energy 95 kcals/396 kj • protein 15 g • carbohydrate 2 g • fat 3 g • fibre 0.2 g • sugar 0.3 g • sodium 0.2 g

⬤ cow's milk-free   ✓ egg-free   ⬤ gluten-free   ⬤ wheat-free   ✓ nut-free   ⬤ vegetarian   ⬤ vegan   ⬤ seafood-free

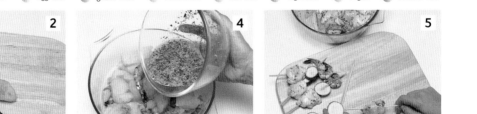

Bean & Cashew Stir-fry

1   Heat a wok or large frying pan, add the oil and, when hot, add the onion and celery and stir–fry gently for 3–4 minutes or until softened.

2   Add the ginger, garlic and chilli to the wok and stir–fry for 30 seconds. Stir in the French beans and mangetout together with the cashew nuts and continue to stir–fry for 1–2 minutes, or until the nuts are golden brown.

3   Dissolve the sugar in the stock, then blend with the sherry, soy sauce and vinegar. Stir into the bean mixture and bring to the boil. Simmer gently, stirring occasionally for 3–4 minutes, or until the beans and mangetout are tender but still crisp and the sauce has thickened slightly. Season to taste with pepper. Transfer to a warmed serving bowl or spoon on to individual plates. Sprinkle with freshly chopped coriander and serve immediately.

Ingredients   SERVES 4

3 tbsp sunflower oil

1 onion, peeled and finely chopped

1 celery stalk, trimmed and chopped

2.5 cm/1 inch piece fresh root
    ginger, peeled and grated

2 garlic cloves, peeled and crushed

1 red chilli, deseeded and
    finely chopped

175 g/6 oz fine French beans,
    trimmed and halved

175 g/6 oz mangetout, sliced
    diagonally into 3

75 g/3 oz unsalted cashew nuts

1 tsp brown sugar

125 ml/4 fl oz vegetable stock

2 tbsp dry sherry

1 tbsp light soy sauce

1 tsp red wine vinegar

freshly ground black pepper

freshly chopped coriander, to garnish

Nutritional details per 100 g energy 129 kcals/537 kj • protein 3 g • carbohydrate 9 g • fat 10 g • fibre 1.9 g • sugar 3.1 g • sodium 0.3 g

✓ cow's milk-free   ✓ egg-free   ● gluten-free   ● wheat-free   ● nut-free   ✓ vegetarian   ● vegan   ✓ seafood-free

Bulghur Wheat Salad with Minty Lemon Dressing

1 Place the bulghur wheat in a saucepan and cover with boiling water.

2 Simmer for about 10 minutes, then drain thoroughly and turn into a serving bowl.

3 Cut the cucumber into small cubes, chop the shallots finely and reserve. Steam the sweetcorn over a pan of boiling water for 10 minutes or until tender. Drain and slice into thick chunks.

4 Cut a cross on the top of each tomato and place in boiling water until their skins start to peel away.

5 Remove the skins and the seeds and cut the tomatoes into small cubes.

6 Make the dressing by briskly whisking all the ingredients in a small bowl until well mixed.

7 When the bulghur wheat has cooled a little, add all the prepared vegetables and stir in the dressing. Season to taste with pepper and serve.

Ingredients   SERVES 4

125 g/4 oz bulghur wheat
10 cm /4 inch piece cucumber
2 shallots, peeled
125 g/4 oz baby sweetcorn
3 ripe but firm tomatoes

For the dressing:

grated rind of 1 lemon
3 tbsp lemon juice
3 tbsp freshly chopped mint
2 tbsp freshly chopped parsley
1–2 tsp clear honey
2 tbsp sunflower oil
freshly ground black pepper

Nutritional details per 100 g   energy 65 kcals/270 kj • protein 2 g • carbohydrate 8 g • fat 3 g • fibre 0.8 g • sugar 3.4 g • sodium 0.3 g

✓ cow's milk-free   ✓ egg-free   ● gluten-free   ● wheat-free   ✓ nut-free   ✓ vegetarian   ● vegan   ✓ seafood-free

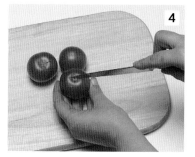

Carrot, Celeriac & Sesame Seed Salad

1 Slice the celeriac into thin matchsticks. Place in a small saucepan of boiling salted water and boil for 2 minutes.

2 Drain and rinse the celeriac in cold water and place in a mixing bowl.

3 Finely grate the carrot. Add the carrot and the raisins to the celeriac in the bowl.

4 Place the sesame seeds under a hot grill or dry-fry in a frying pan for 1–2 minutes until golden brown, then leave to cool.

5 Make the dressing by whisking together the lemon rind, lemon juice, oil, honey, chilli and seasoning or by shaking thoroughly in a screw-topped jar.

6 Pour 2 tablespoons of the dressing over the salad and toss well. Turn into a serving dish and sprinkle over the toasted sesame seeds and chopped parsley. Serve the remaining dressing separately.

Ingredients   SERVES 6

225 g/8 oz celeriac
225 g/8 oz carrots, peeled
50 g/2 oz seedless raisins
2 tbsp sesame seeds
freshly chopped parsley, to garnish

For the lemon & chilli dressing:

grated rind of 1 lemon
4 tbsp lemon juice
2 tbsp sunflower oil
2 tbsp clear honey
1 red bird's-eye chilli, deseeded and
   finely chopped
freshly ground black pepper

Nutritional details per 100 g   energy 95 kcals/395 kj • protein 1 g • carbohydrate 18 g • fat 3 g • fibre trace • sugar 5.1 g • sodium trace
✓ cow's milk-free   ✓ egg-free   ✓ gluten-free   ✓ wheat-free   ✓ nut-free   ✓ vegetarian   ◐ vegan   ✓ seafood-free

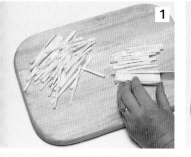

Chicken Noodle Soup

1 Break the chicken carcass into smaller pieces and place in a wok with the carrot, onion, leek, bay leaves, peppercorns and water. Bring slowly to the boil. Skim away any fat or scum that rises for the first 15 minutes. Simmer very gently for 1–1¹/₂ hours. If the liquid reduces by more than one third, add a little more water.

2 Remove from the heat and leave until cold. Strain into a large bowl and chill in the refrigerator until any fat in the stock rises and sets on the surface. Remove the fat and discard. Draw a sheet of absorbent kitchen paper across the surface of the stock to absorb any remaining fat.

3 Return the stock to the wok and bring to a simmer. Add the Chinese cabbage, mushrooms and chicken and simmer gently for 7–8 minutes until the vegetables are tender.

4 Meanwhile, cook the noodles according to the packet instructions until tender. Drain well. Transfer a portion of noodles to each serving bowl before pouring in some soup and vegetables. Serve immediately.

Ingredients   SERVES 4

carcass of a medium–sized
  cooked chicken
1 large carrot, peeled and
  roughly chopped
1 medium onion, peeled
  and quartered
1 leek, trimmed and roughly
  chopped
2–3 bay leaves
a few black peppercorns
2 litres/3¹/₂ pints water
225 g/8 oz Chinese cabbage,
  trimmed
50 g/2 oz chestnut mushrooms,
  wiped and sliced
125 g/4 oz cooked chicken,
  sliced or chopped
50 g/2 oz medium or fine egg
  thread noodles

Nutritional details per 100 g   energy 43 kcals/182 kj · protein 5 g · carbohydrate 4 g · fat 0.8 g · fibre 0.9 g · sugar 2.1 g · sodium trace

✓ cow's milk-free   egg-free   gluten-free   wheat-free   ✓ nut-free   vegetarian   vegan   ✓ seafood-free

Chinese Salad with Soy & Ginger Dressing

1 Rinse and finely shred the Chinese cabbage and place in a serving dish.

2 Slice the water chestnuts into small slivers and cut the spring onions diagonally into 2.5 cm/1 inch lengths, then split lengthways into thin strips.

3 Cut the tomatoes in half and then slice each half into three wedges and reserve.

4 Simmer the mangetout in boiling water for 2 minutes until beginning to soften, drain and cut in half diagonally.

5 Arrange the water chestnuts, spring onions, mangetout, tomatoes and bean sprouts on top of the shredded Chinese cabbage. Garnish with the freshly chopped coriander.

6 Make the dressing by whisking all the ingredients together in a small bowl until mixed thoroughly. Serve with the bread and the salad.

Ingredients   SERVES 4

1 head of Chinese cabbage
200 g can water chestnuts, drained
6 spring onions, trimmed
4 ripe but firm cherry tomatoes
125 g/4 oz mangetout
125 g/4 oz bean sprouts
2 tbsp freshly chopped coriander

For the soy and ginger dressing:

2 tbsp sunflower oil
2 tbsp light soy sauce
2.5 cm/1 inch piece root ginger, peeled and finely grated
zest and juice of 1 lemon
freshly ground black pepper
crusty white bread, to serve

Nutritional details per 100 g   energy 73 kcals/306 kj • protein 2 g • carbohydrate 12 g • fat 2 g • fibre 0.6 g • sugar 1.2 g • sodium 0.5 g

✔ cow's milk-free   ✔ egg-free   ◐ gluten-free   ◐ wheat-free   ✔ nut-free   ✔ vegetarian   ✔ vegan   ✔ seafood-free

2

3

5

Chunky Halibut Casserole

1   Heat the oil in a large saucepan, add the onions and pepper and cook for 5 minutes, or until softened.

2   Cut the peeled potatoes into 2.5 cm/1 inch cubes, rinse lightly and shake dry, then add them to the onions and pepper in the saucepan. Add the courgettes and cook, stirring frequently, for a further 2–3 minutes.

3   Sprinkle the flour, paprika and vegetable oil into the saucepan and cook, stirring continuously, for 1 minute. Pour in the stock and the chopped tomatoes, and bring to the boil.

4   Add the basil to the casserole, season to taste with pepper and cover. Simmer for 15 minutes, then add the halibut and simmer very gently for a further 5–7 minutes, or until the fish and vegetables are just tender.

5   Garnish with basil sprigs and serve immediately with freshly cooked rice.

Ingredients   SERVES 6

1 tbsp olive oil
2 large onions, peeled and sliced
   into rings
1 red pepper, deseeded and
   roughly chopped
450 g/1 lb potatoes, peeled
450 g/1 lb courgettes, trimmed
   and thickly sliced
2 tbsp plain flour
1 tbsp paprika
2 tsp vegetable oil
150 ml/$^1/_4$ pint fish stock
400 g can chopped tomatoes
2 tbsp freshly chopped basil
freshly ground black pepper
450 g/1 lb halibut fillet, skinned and
   cut into 2.5 cm/1 inch cubes
sprigs of fresh basil, to garnish
freshly cooked rice, to serve

Nutritional details per 100 g   energy 72 kcals/307 kj • protein 6 g • carbohydrate 11 g • fat 1 g • fibre 0.9 g • sugar 2.1 g • sodium trace

✓ cow's milk-free   ✓ egg-free   ● gluten-free   ● wheat-free   ✓ nut-free   ● vegetarian   ● vegan   ● seafood-free

Pad Thai

1. To make the sauce, whisk all the sauce ingredients in a bowl and reserve. Put the rice noodles in a large bowl and pour over enough hot water to cover. Leave to stand for about 15 minutes until softened. Drain and rinse, then drain again.

2. Heat the oil in a wok over a high heat until hot, but not smoking. Add the chicken strips and stir-fry constantly until they begin to colour. Using a slotted spoon, transfer to a plate. Reduce the heat to medium–high.

3. Add the shallots, garlic and spring onions and stir-fry for 1 minute. Stir in the rice noodles, then the reserved sauce and mix well.

4. Add the reserved chicken strips with the crab meat or prawns, bean sprouts and radish and stir well. Cook for about 5 minutes, stirring frequently, until heated through. If the noodles begin to stick, add a little water.

5. Turn into a large, shallow serving dish and sprinkle with the chopped peanuts, if using. Serve immediately.

Ingredients   SERVES 4

225 g/8 oz flat rice noodles
2 tbsp vegetable oil
225 g/8 oz boneless chicken breast, skinned and thinly sliced
4 shallots, peeled and thinly sliced
2 garlic cloves, peeled and finely chopped
4 spring onions, trimmed and diagonally cut into 5 cm/2 inch pieces
350 g/12 oz fresh white crab meat or tiny prawns
75 g/3 oz fresh bean sprouts, rinsed and drained
2 tbsp preserved or fresh radish
2–3 tbsp roasted peanuts, chopped (optional)

For the sauce:

2 tbsp Thai fish sauce (nam pla)
2–3 tbsp rice vinegar or cider vinegar
1 tbsp chilli bean or oyster sauce
1 tbsp toasted sesame oil
1 tbsp light brown sugar
1 red chilli, deseeded and thinly sliced

Nutritional details per 100 g energy 129 kcals/540 kj • protein 13 g • carbohydrate 8 g • fat 5 g • fibre 0.5 g • sugar 2.3 g • sodium 0.6 g

✓ cow's milk-free   ✓ egg-free   ● gluten-free   ● wheat-free   ● nut-free   ● vegetarian   ● vegan   ● seafood-free

Pasta with Courgettes, Rosemary & Lemon

1 Bring a large saucepan of salted water to the boil and add the pasta.

2 Return to the boil and cook until 'al dente' or according to the packet instructions.

3 When the pasta is almost done, heat the oil in a large frying pan and add the garlic.

4 Cook over a medium heat until the garlic just begins to brown. Be careful not to overcook the garlic at this stage or it will become bitter.

5 Add the courgettes, rosemary, parsley and lemon zest and juice. Cook for 3–4 minutes until the courgettes are just tender.

6 Add the olives to the frying pan and stir well. Season to taste with pepper and remove from the heat.

7 Drain the pasta well and add to the frying pan. Stir until thoroughly combined. Garnish with lemon and sprigs of fresh rosemary and serve immediately.

Ingredients   SERVES 4

350 g/12 oz dried pasta shapes, e.g. rigatoni

1¹/₂ tbsp good quality extra virgin olive oil

2 garlic cloves, peeled and finely chopped

4 medium courgettes, thinly sliced

1 tbsp freshly chopped rosemary

1 tbsp freshly chopped parsley

zest and juice of 2 lemons

25 g/1 oz pitted black olives, roughly chopped

25 g/1 oz pitted green olives, roughly chopped

freshly ground black pepper

To garnish:

lemon slices

sprigs of fresh rosemary

Nutritional details per 100 g energy 85 kcals/360 kj • protein 3 g • carbohydrate 14 g • fat 3 g • fibre 1.1 g • sugar 1 g • sodium trace

✓ cow's milk-free   ✓ egg-free   ● gluten-free   ● wheat-free   ✓ nut-free   ✓ vegetarian   ✓ vegan   ✓ seafood-free

Rice with Squash & Sage

1. Peel the squash, cut in half lengthways and remove the seeds and stringy flesh. Cut the remaining flesh into small cubes and reserve.

2. Heat the wok, add the oil and heat until bubbling, then add the onion, garlic and sage and stir-fry for 1 minute.

3. Add the squash to the wok and stir-fry for a further 10–12 minutes, or until the squash is tender. Remove from the heat.

4. Meanwhile, bring the vegetable stock to the boil and add the rice. Cook for 8–10 minutes, or until the rice is just tender but still quite wet.

5. Add the cooked rice to the squash mixture. Stir in the pine nuts and season to taste with pepper. Garnish with snipped chives and serve immediately.

Ingredients   SERVES 4–6

450 g/1 lb butternut squash
2 tbsp olive oil
1 small onion, peeled and
   finely chopped
3 garlic cloves, peeled and crushed
2 tbsp freshly chopped sage
1 litre/1³/₄ pints vegetable stock
450 g/1 lb Arborio rice
50 g/2 oz pine nuts, toasted
freshly snipped chives, to garnish
freshly ground black pepper

Nutritional details per 100 g   energy 107 kcals/446 kj · protein 2 g · carbohydrate 14 g · fat 5 g · fibre 0.2 g · sugar 0.6 g · sodium 0.3 g

✓ cow's milk-free   ✓ egg-free   gluten-free   wheat-free   nut-free   ✓ vegetarian   ✓ vegan   ✓ seafood-free

Salmon Noisettes with Fruity Sauce

1 Using a sharp knife, cut the bone away from each salmon steak to create two salmon fillets each. Shape the salmon fillets into noisettes and secure with fine string.

2 Mix together the citrus rinds and juices, olive oil, honey, wholegrain mustard and pepper in a shallow dish. Add the salmon fillets and turn to coat. Cover and leave to marinate in the refrigerator for 4 hours, turning them occasionally in the marinade.

3 Heat the wok then add the sunflower oil and heat until hot. Lift out the salmon noisettes, reserving the marinade. Add the salmon to the wok and cook for 6–10 minutes, turning once during cooking, until the fish is cooked through and just flaking. Pour the marinade into the wok and heat through gently.

4 Mix together the salad leaves, watercress and tomatoes and arrange on serving plates. Top with the salmon noisettes and drizzle over any remaining warm marinade. Serve immediately.

Ingredients   SERVES 4

4 x 125 g/4 oz salmon steaks
juice and grated rind of 2 lemons
juice and grated rind of 1 lime
3 tbsp olive oil
1 tbsp clear honey
1 tbsp wholegrain mustard
freshly ground black pepper
1 tbsp sunflower oil
125 g/4 oz mixed salad leaves,
    washed
1 bunch watercress, washed and
    thick stalks removed
250 g/9 oz baby plum
    tomatoes, halved

Nutritional details per 100 g energy 129 kcals/537 kj • protein 10 g • carbohydrate 5 g • fat 9 g • fibre 0.3 g • sugar 2 g • sodium trace

✓ cow's milk-free   ✓ egg-free   ● gluten-free   ● wheat-free   ✓ nut-free   ● vegetarian   ● vegan   ● seafood-free

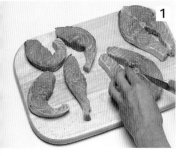

Salmon with Herbed Potatoes

1 Preheat the oven to 190°C/375°F/Gas Mark 5, about 10 minutes before required. Parboil the potatoes in lightly salted boiling water for 5–8 minutes until they are barely tender. Drain and reserve.

2 Cut out four pieces of baking parchment paper, measuring 20.5 cm/8 inches square, and place on the work surface. Arrange the parboiled potatoes on top. Wipe the salmon steaks and place on top of the potatoes.

3 Place the carrot strips in a bowl with the asparagus spears, sugar snaps and grated lemon rind and juice. Season to taste with salt and pepper. Toss lightly together.

4 Divide the vegetables evenly between the salmon parcels. Drizzle the top of each parcel with olive oil and add a sprig of parsley.

5 To wrap a parcel, lift up two opposite sides of the paper and fold the edges together. Twist the paper at the other two ends to seal the parcel well. Repeat with the remaining parcels.

6 Place the parcels on a baking tray and bake in the preheated oven for 15 minutes. Place an unopened parcel on each plate and open just before eating.

Ingredients SERVES 4

450 g/1 lb baby new potatoes
freshly ground black pepper
4 salmon steaks, each weighing
   about 175 g/6 oz
1 carrot, peeled and cut into
   fine strips
175 g/6 oz asparagus spears,
   trimmed
175 g/6 oz sugar snap peas, trimmed
juice and finely grated rind of
   1 lemon
1 tbsp olive oil
4 large sprigs of fresh parsley

Nutritional details per 100 g energy 111 kcals/464 kj · protein 10 g · carbohydrate 6 g · fat 6 g · fibre 1.1 g · sugar 0.9 g · sodium trace

✓ cow's milk–free   ✓ egg–free   ✓ gluten–free   ✓ wheat–free   ✓ nut–free   ● vegetarian   ● vegan   ● seafood–free

Spicy Cucumber Stir-fry

1 Rinse the soaked beans thoroughly, then drain. Place in a saucepan, cover with cold water and bring to the boil, skimming off any scum that rises to the surface. Boil for 10 minutes, then reduce the heat and simmer for 1–1$^1/_2$ hours. Drain and reserve.

2 Peel the cucumbers, slice lengthways and remove the seeds. Cut into 2.5 cm/1 inch slices.

3 Heat a wok or large frying pan, add the oil and when hot, add the chilli powder, garlic and black beans and stir–fry for 30 seconds.

4 Add the cucumber and stir–fry for 20 seconds.

5 Pour the stock into the wok and cook for 3–4 minutes, or until the cucumber is very tender. The liquid will have evaporated at this stage.

6 Remove from the heat and stir in the sesame oil. Turn into a warmed serving dish, garnish with chopped parsley and serve immediately.

Ingredients SERVES 4

25 g/1 oz black soya beans, soaked
  in cold water overnight
1$^1/_2$ cucumbers
1 tbsp vegetable oil
$^1/_2$ tsp mild chilli powder
4 garlic cloves, peeled and crushed
5 tbsp vegetable stock
1 tsp sesame oil
1 tbsp freshly chopped parsley,
  to garnish

Nutritional details per 100 g   energy 61 kcals/251 kj • protein 2 g • carbohydrate 3 g • fat 5 g • fibre 0.6 g • sugar 0.2 g • sodium 0.2 g

✔ cow's milk-free   ✔ egg-free   ◑ gluten-free   ✔ wheat-free   ✔ nut-free   ✔ vegetarian   ✔ vegan   ✔ seafood-free

Stir-fried Chicken with Spinach, Tomatoes & Pine Nuts

1 Heat the wok and add the pine nuts. Dry–fry for about 2 minutes, shaking often to ensure that they toast but do not burn. Remove and reserve. Wipe any dust from the wok.

2 Heat the wok again, add the oil and, when hot, add the red onion and stir–fry for 2 minutes. Add the chicken and stir–fry for 2–3 minutes, or until golden brown. Reduce the heat, toss in the cherry tomatoes and stir–fry gently until the tomatoes start to disintegrate.

3 Add the baby spinach and stir–fry for 2–3 minutes, or until they start to wilt. Season to taste with pepper, then sprinkle in the grated nutmeg and drizzle in the balsamic vinegar. Finally, stir in the raisins and reserved toasted pine nuts. Serve immediately on a bed of ribbon noodles.

Ingredients SERVES 4

50 g/2 oz pine nuts
2 tbsp sunflower oil
1 red onion, peeled and finely chopped
450 g/1 lb skinless, boneless chicken breast fillets, cut into strips
450 g/1 lb cherry tomatoes, halved
225 g/8 oz baby spinach, washed
freshly ground black pepper
1/4 tsp freshly grated nutmeg
2 tbsp balsamic vinegar
50 g/2 oz raisins
freshly cooked ribbon noodles, to serve

Nutritional details per 100 g energy 120 kcals/503 kj ● protein 10 g ● carbohydrate 9 g ● fat 5 g ● fibre 1.2 g ● sugar 3.7 g ● sodium trace

✓ cow's milk-free ✓ egg-free ● gluten-free ● wheat-free ● nut-free ● vegetarian ● vegan ✓ seafood-free

Sardines with Redcurrants

1 Preheat the grill and line the grill rack with foil 2–3 minutes before cooking.

2 Warm the redcurrant jelly in a bowl standing over a pan of gently simmering water and stir until smooth. Add the lime rind and sherry to the bowl and stir well until blended.

3 Lightly rinse the sardines and pat dry with absorbent kitchen paper.

4 Place on a chopping board and, with a sharp knife, make several diagonal cuts across the flesh of each fish. Season the sardines inside the cavities with pepper.

5 Gently brush the warm marinade over the skin and inside the cavities of the sardines.

6 Place on the grill rack and cook under the preheated grill for 8–10 minutes, or until the fish are cooked. Carefully turn the sardines over at least once during grilling and baste occasionally with the remaining redcurrant and lime marinade.

7 Garnish with the redcurrants and serve immediately with the salad and lime wedges.

Ingredients SERVES 4

2 tbsp redcurrant jelly
finely grated rind of 1 lime
2 tbsp medium dry sherry
450 g/1 lb fresh sardines, cleaned
    and heads removed
freshly ground black pepper
lime wedges, to garnish

To serve:
fresh redcurrants
fresh green salad

Nutritional details per 100 g energy 137 kcals/573 kj • protein 13 g • carbohydrate 7 g • fat 7 g • fibre 0.2 g • sugar 5 g • sodium 0.1 g

✓ cow's milk-free   ✓ egg-free   ✓ gluten-free   ✓ wheat-free   ✓ nut-free   ◐ vegetarian   ◐ vegan   ● seafood-free

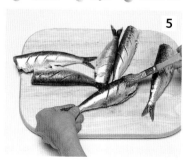

Turkey & Tomato Tagine

1 Preheat the oven to 190°C/375°F/Gas Mark 5. Put all the ingredients for the meatballs in a bowl, except the oil and mix well. Season to taste with salt and pepper. Shape into 20 balls, about the size of walnuts. Put on a tray, cover lightly and chill in the refrigerator while making the sauce.

2 Put the onion and garlic in a pan with 125 ml/4 fl oz of the stock. Cook over a low heat until all the stock has evaporated. Continue cooking for 1 minute, or until the onions begin to colour.

3 Add the remaining stock to the pan with the tomatoes, cumin, cinnamon and cayenne pepper. Simmer for 10 minutes, until slightly thickened and reduced. Stir in the parsley and season to taste.

4 Heat the oil in a large, non–stick frying pan and cook the meatballs in two batches until lightly browned all over.

5 Lift the meatballs out with a slotted spoon and drain on kitchen paper.

6 Pour the sauce into a tagine or an ovenproof casserole. Top with the meatballs, cover and cook in the preheated oven for 25–30 minutes, or until the meatballs are cooked through and the sauce is bubbling. Garnish with freshly chopped herbs and serve immediately on a bed of couscous or plain boiled rice.

Ingredients   SERVES 4

For the meatballs:

450 g/1 lb fresh turkey mince
1 small onion, peeled and very
    finely chopped
1 garlic clove, peeled and crushed
1 tbsp freshly chopped coriander
1 tsp ground cumin
1 tbsp olive oil
freshly ground black pepper

For the sauce:

1 onion, peeled and finely chopped
1 garlic clove, peeled and crushed
150 ml/$^1/_4$ pint turkey stock
400 g can chopped tomatoes
$^1/_2$ tsp ground cumin
$^1/_2$ tsp ground cinnamon
pinch of cayenne pepper
freshly chopped parsley
freshly chopped herbs, to garnish
freshly cooked couscous or rice,
    to serve

Nutritional details per 100 g   energy 94 kcals/394 kj • protein 12 g • carbohydrate 8 g • fat 2 g • fibre 0.5 g • sugar 1.7 g • sodium trace

✓ cow's milk–free   ✓ egg–free   ◖ gluten–free   ◖ wheat–free   ✓ nut–free   ◖ vegetarian   ◖ vegan   ✓ seafood–free

1

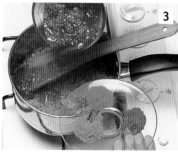
3

6

Zesty Whole-baked Fish

1 Preheat the oven to 220°C/425°F/Gas Mark 7. Lightly rinse the fish and pat dry with absorbent kitchen paper. Season the cavity with a little pepper. Make several diagonal cuts across the flesh of the fish and season.

2 Mix together the low-fat spread, garlic, lemon and orange zest and juice, nutmeg, mustard and fresh breadcrumbs. Mix well together. Spoon the breadcrumb mixture into the slits with a small sprig of dill. Place the remaining herbs inside the fish cavity. Weigh the fish and calculate the cooking time – allow 10 minutes per 450 g/1 lb.

3 Lay the fish onto a double thickness of foil. If liked, smear the fish with a little low-fat spread. Top with the lime slices and fold the foil into a parcel. Chill in the refrigerator for about 15 minutes.

4 Place in a roasting tin and cook in the preheated oven for the calculated cooking time. Fifteen minutes before the end of cooking, open the foil and return until the skin begins to crisp. Remove the fish from the oven and stand for 10 minutes.

5 Pour the juices from the roasting tin into a saucepan. Bring to the boil and stir in the crème fraîche and fromage frais. Simmer for 3 minutes or until hot. Garnish with dill sprigs and serve immediately.

Ingredients   SERVES 4

1.8 kg/4 lb whole salmon, cleaned
freshly ground black pepper
50 g/2 oz low-fat spread
1 garlic clove, peeled and
    finely sliced
zest and juice of 1 lemon
zest of 1 orange
1 tsp freshly grated nutmeg
3 tbsp Dijon mustard
2 tbsp fresh white breadcrumbs
2 bunches fresh dill
1 bunch fresh tarragon
1 lime, sliced
150 ml/¼ pint half-fat
    crème fraîche
450 ml/¾ pint fromage frais
dill sprigs, to garnish

Nutritional details per 100 g energy 193 kcals/805 kj • protein 21 g • carbohydrate 2 g • fat 12 g • fibre 0.1 g • sugar 0.4 g • sodium 0.2 g

cow's milk-free ✓ egg-free gluten-free wheat-free ✓ nut-free vegetarian vegan seafood-free

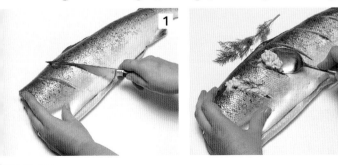

Allergy-free

Food allergies and food intolerances can trigger a whole range of unpleasant symptoms. This section includes recipes that help you to avoid some of the more common allergens such as nuts, cow's milk, egg whites, gluten, berries, soya beans and fish & shellfish. If you suspect that you have a food allergy it is important that you get tested so that you can use the recipes that avoid this particular food.

Braised Rabbit with Red Peppers

1. Place the rabbit pieces in a shallow dish with half the olive oil, the lemon zest and juice, thyme and some black pepper. Turn until well coated, then cover and leave to marinate for about 1 hour.

2. Heat half the remaining oil in a large, heavy-based casserole, add the onion and cook for 5 minutes, then add the peppers and cook for a further 12–15 minutes, or until softened, stirring occasionally. Stir in the garlic, crushed tomatoes and brown sugar and cook, covered, until soft, stirring occasionally.

3. Heat the remaining oil in a large frying pan, drain the rabbit, reserving the marinade, and pat the rabbit dry with absorbent kitchen paper. Add the rabbit to the pan and cook on all sides until golden. Transfer the rabbit to the casserole and mix to cover with the tomato sauce.

4. Add the reserved marinade to the frying pan, stirring to loosen any browned bits from the pan. Add to the rabbit and stir gently.

5. Cover the pan and simmer for 30 minutes or until the rabbit is tender. Serve the rabbit and the vegetable mixture on a bed of polenta or creamy mashed potatoes.

Ingredients   SERVES 4

1.1 kg/2^1/$_2$ lb rabbit pieces
125 ml/4 fl oz olive oil
juice and grated zest of 1 lemon
2–3 tbsp freshly chopped thyme
salt and freshly ground black pepper
1 onion, peeled and thinly sliced
4 red peppers, deseeded and cut
    into 2.5 cm/1 inch pieces
2 garlic cloves, peeled and crushed
400 g can strained,
    crushed tomatoes
1 tsp brown sugar
freshly cooked polenta or creamy
    mashed potatoes, to serve

Nutritional details per 100 g energy 105 kcals/440 kj · protein 10 g · carbohydrate 4 g · fat 6 g · fibre 0.7 g · sugar 3 g · sodium 0.04 g

✔ cow's milk-free   ✔ egg-free   ✔ gluten-free   ✔ wheat-free   ✔ nut-free   ◐ vegetarian   ◐ vegan   ✔ seafood-free

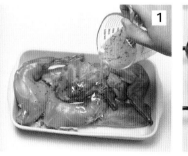

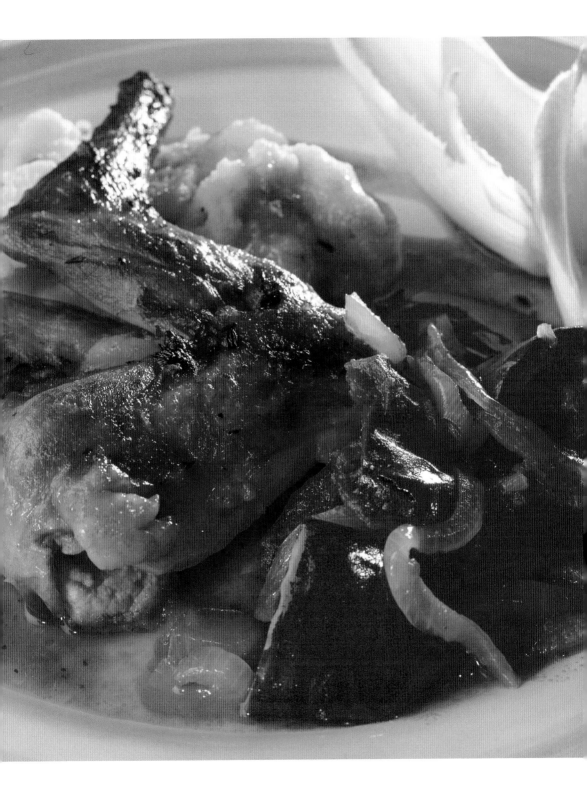

Chilli Roast Chicken

1 Preheat the oven to 190°C/375°F/Gas Mark 5. Roughly chop the chillies and put in a food processor with the turmeric, cumin seeds, coriander seeds, garlic, ginger, lemon juice, olive oil, coriander, salt, pepper and 2 tablespoons of cold water. Blend to a paste, leaving the ingredients still slightly chunky.

2 Starting at the neck end of the chicken, gently ease up the skin to loosen it from the breast. Reserve 3 tablespoons of the paste. Push the remaining paste over the chicken breast under the skin, spreading it evenly.

3 Put the chicken into a large roasting tin. Mix the reserved chilli paste with the melted margarine. Brush 1 tablespoon of it evenly over the chicken and roast in the preheated oven for 20 minutes.

4 Meanwhile, halve, peel and scoop out the seeds from the butternut squash. Cut into large chunks and mix in the remaining chilli paste and margarine mixture.

5 Arrange the butternut squash around the chicken. Roast for a further hour, basting with the cooking juices about every 20 minutes until the chicken is fully cooked and the squash tender. Garnish with parsley and coriander. Serve hot with baked potatoes and green vegetables.

Ingredients   SERVES 4

3 medium–hot fresh red chillies, deseeded
$1/2$ tsp ground turmeric
1 tsp cumin seeds
1 tsp coriander seeds
2 garlic cloves, peeled and crushed
2.5 cm/1 inch piece fresh root ginger, peeled and chopped
1 tbsp lemon juice
1 tbsp olive oil
2 tbsp fresh coriander, roughly chopped
$1/2$ tsp salt
freshly ground black pepper
1.4 kg/3 lb oven–ready chicken
15 g/$1/2$ oz dairy–free margarine, melted
550 g/$1^1/4$ lb butternut squash
fresh parsley and coriander sprigs, to garnish

To serve:
4 baked potatoes
seasonal green vegetables

Nutritional details per 100 g   energy 168 kcals/704 kj • protein 16 g • carbohydrate 4 g • fat 10 g • fibre 0.02 g • sugar 0.02 g • sodium 0.1 g

✔ cow's milk-free   ✔ egg-free   ✔ gluten-free   ✔ wheat-free   ✔ nut-free   ○ vegetarian   ○ vegan   ✔ seafood-free

 **1**
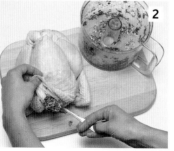 **2**
 **4**

Chinese-glazed Poussin with Green & Black Rice

1 Preheat the oven to 200°C/400°F/Gas Mark 6, 15 minutes before cooking. Rinse the poussins inside and out and pat dry with kitchen paper. Using tweezers, remove any feathers. Season well with salt and pepper, then reserve. Pour the apple juice into a small saucepan and add the cinnamon stick, star anise and Chinese five-spice powder. Bring to the boil, then simmer rapidly until reduced by half. Reduce the heat, stir in the sugar, tomato purée, vinegar and orange rind and simmer gently until the sugar is dissolved and the glaze is syrupy. Remove from the heat and leave to cool completely. Remove the whole spices.

2 Place the poussins on a wire rack set over a foil-lined roasting tin. Brush generously with the apple glaze. Roast for 40–45 minutes, or until the juices run clear when the thigh is pierced with a skewer, basting once or twice with the remaining glaze. Remove the poussins from the oven and leave to cool slightly.

3 Meanwhile, cook the rice according to the packet instructions. Bring a large saucepan of lightly salted water to the boil and add the mangetout. Blanch for 1 minute, then drain thoroughly. As soon as the rice is cooked, drain and transfer to a warmed bowl. Add the mangetout and spring onions, season to taste and stir well. Arrange on warmed plates, place a poussin on top and serve immediately.

Ingredients   SERVES 4

4 oven-ready poussins
salt and freshly ground black pepper
300 ml/$^{1}/_{2}$ pint apple juice
1 cinnamon stick
2 star anise
$^{1}/_{2}$ tsp Chinese five-spice powder
50 g/2 oz dark muscovado sugar
2 tbsp tomato purée
1 tbsp cider vinegar
grated rind of 1 orange
350 g/12 oz mixed basmati and
    wild rice
125 g/4 oz mangetout, finely
    sliced lengthways
1 bunch spring onions, trimmed and
    finely shredded lengthways

Nutritional details per 100 g   energy 178 kcals/744 kj • protein 17 g • carbohydrate 6 g • fat 9 g • fibre 0.2 g • sugar 2 g • sodium 0.08 g

✓ cow's milk-free   ✓ egg-free   ✓ gluten-free   ✓ wheat-free   ✓ nut-free   ◐ vegetarian   ◐ vegan   ✓ seafood-free

1

2

3

Chinese Leaf & Mushroom Soup

1 Trim the stem ends of the Chinese leaves and cut in half lengthways. Remove the triangular core with a knife, then cut into 2.5 cm/1 inch slices and reserve.

2 Place the dried Chinese mushrooms in a bowl and pour over enough almost-boiling water to cover. Leave to stand for 20 minutes to soften, then gently lift out and squeeze out the liquid. Discard the stems and thinly slice the caps and reserve. Strain the liquid through a muslin-lined sieve or a coffee filter paper and reserve.

3 Heat a wok over a medium–high heat, add the oil and, when hot, add the bacon. Stir-fry for 3–4 minutes, or until crisp and golden, stirring frequently. Add the ginger and chestnut mushrooms and stir-fry for a further 2–3 minutes. Add the chicken stock and bring to the boil, skimming off any fat and scum that rises to the surface. Add the spring onions, sherry or rice wine, Chinese leaves, sliced Chinese mushrooms and season to taste with salt and pepper. Pour in the reserved soaking liquid and reduce the heat to the lowest possible setting.

4 Simmer gently, covered, until all the vegetables are very tender; this will take about 10 minutes. Add a little water if the liquid has reduced too much. Spoon into soup bowls and drizzle with a little sesame oil. Serve immediately.

Ingredients   SERVES 4–6

450 g/1 lb Chinese leaves

25 g/1 oz dried Chinese (shiitake) mushrooms

1 tbsp vegetable oil

75 g/3 oz smoked streaky bacon, diced

2.5 cm/1 inch piece fresh root ginger, peeled and finely chopped

175 g/6 oz chestnut mushrooms, thinly sliced

1.1 litres/2 pints gluten-free chicken stock

4–6 spring onions, trimmed and cut into short lengths

2 tbsp dry sherry or Chinese rice wine

salt and freshly ground black pepper

sesame oil for drizzling

Nutritional details per 100 g energy 72 kcals/297 kj • protein 4 g • carbohydrate 4 g • fat 5 g • fibre 0.09 g • sugar 0.6 g • sodium 0.55 g

✓ cow's milk-free   ✓ egg-free   ✓ gluten-free   ✓ wheat-free   ✓ nut-free   ○ vegetarian   ○ vegan   ✓ seafood-free

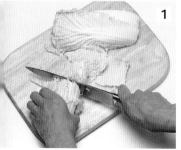

Coconut-baked Courgettes

1 Preheat the oven to 180°C/350°F/Gas Mark 4, 10 minutes before cooking. Lightly oil a 1.4 litre/2½ pint ovenproof gratin dish. Heat a wok, add the oil and, when hot, add the onion and stir-fry for 2–3 minutes. Add the garlic, chilli powder and coriander and stir-fry for 1–2 minutes.

2 Pour 300 ml/½ pint cold water into the wok and bring to the boil. Add the coconut and tomato purée and simmer for 3–4 minutes; most of the water will evaporate at this stage. Spoon 4 tablespoons of the spice and coconut mixture into a small bowl and reserve.

3 Stir the courgettes into the remaining spice and coconut mixture and spoon into the oiled gratin dish. Sprinkle the reserved spice and coconut mixture evenly over the top. Bake, uncovered, in the preheated oven for 15–20 minutes, or until golden. Garnish with chopped parsley and serve.

Please note that coconut is fine for most nut allergy sufferers, but please check with your doctor if you have any concerns.

Ingredients SERVES 4

3 tbsp sunflower oil
1 onion, peeled and finely sliced
4 garlic cloves, peeled and crushed
½ tsp chilli powder
1 tsp ground coriander
6–8 tbsp desiccated coconut
1 tbsp tomato purée
700 g/1½ lb courgettes,
    thinly sliced
freshly chopped parsley, to garnish

Nutritional details per 100 g   energy 112 kcals/468 kj • protein 3 g • carbohydrate 4 g • fat 10 g • fibre 2 g • sugar 3 g • sodium trace

✓ cow's milk-free   ✓ egg-free   ✓ gluten-free   ✓ wheat-free   ✓ nut-free   ✓ vegetarian   ✓ vegan   ✓ seafood-free

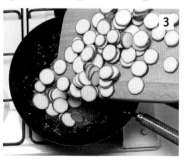

Coconut Beef

1 Trim off any fat or gristle from the beef and cut into thin strips. Heat a wok or large frying pan, add 2 tablespoons of the oil and heat until just smoking. Add the beef and cook for 5–8 minutes, turning occasionally, until browned on all sides. Using a slotted spoon, transfer the beef to a plate and keep warm.

2 Add the remaining oil to the wok and heat until almost smoking. Add the spring onions, chilli, garlic and ginger and cook for 1 minute, stirring occasionally. Add the mushrooms and stir–fry for 3 minutes. Using a slotted spoon, transfer the mushroom mixture to a plate and keep warm.

3 Return the beef to the wok and pour in the coconut cream and stock. Bring to the boil and simmer for 3–4 minutes, or until the juices are slightly reduced and the beef is just tender.

4 Return the mushroom mixture to the wok and heat through. Stir in the chopped coriander and season to taste with salt and pepper. Serve immediately with freshly cooked rice.

Ingredients SERVES 4

450 g/1 lb beef rump or sirloin steak
4 tbsp sunflower oil
2 bunches spring onions, trimmed and thickly sliced
1 red chilli, deseeded and chopped
1 garlic clove, peeled and chopped
2 cm/1 inch piece fresh root ginger, peeled and cut into matchsticks
125 g/4 oz shiitake mushrooms
200 ml/7 fl oz coconut cream
150 ml/¼ pint chicken stock
4 tbsp freshly chopped coriander
salt and freshly ground black pepper
freshly cooked rice, to serve

Nutritional details per 100 g energy 243 kcals/1013 kj • protein 13 g • carbohydrate 12 g • fat 17 g • fibre 0.2 g • sugar 1 g • sodium 0.1 g

✓ cow's milk–free   ✓ egg–free   ✓ gluten–free   ✓ wheat–free   ✓ nut–free   ◖ vegetarian   ◖ vegan   ✓ seafood–free

Coconut Chicken Soup

1 Discard the outer leaves of the lemon grass stalks, then place onto a chopping board and, using a mallet or rolling pin, pound gently to bruise and reserve.

2 Heat the vegetable oil in a large saucepan and cook the onions over a medium heat for about 10–15 minutes until soft and beginning to change colour.

3 Lower the heat, stir in the garlic, ginger, lime leaves and turmeric and cook for 1 minute. Add the red pepper, coconut milk, stock, lemon grass and rice. Bring to the boil, cover and simmer gently over a low heat for about 10 minutes.

4 Cut the chicken into bite-sized pieces, then stir into the soup, with the sweetcorn and the freshly chopped coriander. Reheat gently, stirring frequently. Serve immediately with a few chopped pickled chillies to sprinkle on top.

Ingredients SERVES 4

2 lemon grass stalks
3 tbsp vegetable oil
3 medium onions, peeled and
    finely sliced
3 garlic cloves, peeled and crushed
2 tbsp fresh root ginger, finely grated
2–3 kaffir lime leaves
1¹/₂ tsp turmeric
1 red pepper, deseeded and diced
400 ml can coconut milk
1.1 litres/2 pints gluten-free
    vegetable or chicken stock
250 g/9 oz easy-cook
    long-grain rice
275 g/10 oz cooked chicken meat
285 g can sweetcorn, drained
3 tbsp freshly chopped coriander
freshly chopped pickled chillies,
    to serve

Nutritional details per 100 g energy 121 kcals/510 kj • protein 7 g • carbohydrate 14 g • fat 4 g • fibre 0.7 g • sugar 4.1 g • sodium 0.2 g

✓ cow's milk-free   ✓ egg-free   ✓ gluten-free   ✓ wheat-free   ✓ nut-free   ● vegetarian   ● vegan   ✓ seafood-free

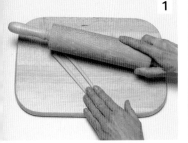

1

3

4

Fried Rice with Bamboo Shoots & Ginger

1 Heat a wok, add the oil and, when hot, add the onion and cook gently for 3–4 minutes. Add the long–grain rice and cook for 3–4 minutes or until golden, stirring frequently.

2 Add the garlic, ginger and chopped spring onions to the wok and stir well. Pour the vegetable stock into a small saucepan and bring to the boil. Carefully ladle the hot stock into the wok, stir well, then simmer gently for 10 minutes or until most of the liquid has been absorbed.

3 Stir the button mushrooms and peas into the wok and continue to cook for a further 5 minutes, or until the rice is tender, adding a little extra stock if necessary.

4 Add the bamboo shoots to the wok and carefully stir in. Season to taste with salt and pepper. Cook for 2–3 minutes or until heated through. Tip onto a warmed serving dish, garnish with coriander leaves and serve immediately.

Ingredients   SERVES 4

4 tbsp sunflower oil

1 onion, peeled and finely chopped

225 g/8 oz long–grain rice

3 garlic cloves, peeled and cut
    into slivers

2.5 cm/1 inch piece fresh root
    ginger, peeled and grated

3 spring onions, trimmed
    and chopped

450 ml/$^3/_4$ pint gluten–free
    vegetable stock

125 g/4 oz button mushrooms,
    wiped and halved

75 g/3 oz frozen peas, thawed

500 g can bamboo shoots, drained
    and thinly sliced

salt and freshly ground black pepper

fresh coriander leaves, to garnish

Nutritional details per 100 g energy 92 kcals/381 kj · protein 2 g · carbohydrate 10 g · fat 5 g · fibre 0.5 g · sugar 0.7 g · sodium 0.2 g

✓ cow's milk-free   ✓ egg-free   ✓ gluten–free   ✓ wheat–free   ✓ nut–free   ✓ vegetarian   ✓ vegan   ✓ seafood-free

Ginger & Garlic Potatoes

1 Scrub the potatoes, then place, unpeeled, in a large saucepan and cover with boiling salted water. Bring to the boil and cook for 15 minutes, then drain and leave the potatoes to cool completely. Peel and cut into 2.5 cm/1 inch cubes.

2 Place the root ginger, garlic, turmeric and salt in a food processor and blend for 1 minute. With the motor still running, slowly add 3 tablespoons of water and blend into a paste. Alternatively, pound the ingredients to a paste with a pestle and mortar.

3 Heat the oil in a large heavy-based frying pan and, when hot, but not smoking, add the fennel seeds and fry for a few minutes. Stir in the ginger paste and cook for 2 minutes, stirring frequently. Take care not to burn the mixture.

4 Reduce the heat, then add the potatoes and cook for 5–7 minutes, stirring frequently, until the potatoes have a golden brown crust. Add the diced apple and spring onions, then sprinkle with the freshly chopped coriander. Heat through for 2 minutes, then serve on assorted salad leaves.

Ingredients   SERVES 4

700 g/1^1/$_2$ lb potatoes
2.5 cm/1 inch piece of root ginger, peeled and coarsely chopped
3 garlic cloves, peeled and chopped
^{1}/$_2$ tsp turmeric
1 tsp salt
5 tbsp vegetable oil
1 tsp whole fennel seeds
1 large eating apple, cored and diced
6 spring onions, trimmed and sliced diagonally
1 tbsp coriander, freshly chopped

To serve:

assorted bitter salad leaves

Nutritional details per 100 g energy 116 kcals/487 kj • protein 2 g • carbohydrate 15 g • fat 6 g • fibre 1 g • sugar 0.7 g • sodium 0.2 g

✔ cow's milk-free   ✔ egg-free   ✔ gluten-free   ✔ wheat-free   ✔ nut-free   ✔ vegetarian   ✔ vegan   ✔ seafood-free

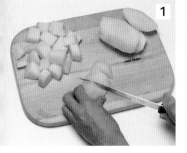

Hot-&-Sour Duck

1 Sprinkle the duck with the salt, cover lightly and refrigerate for 20 minutes.

2 Meanwhile, place the tamarind pulp in a small bowl, pour over 4 tablespoons of hot water and leave for 2–3 minutes or until softened. Press the mixture through a sieve into another bowl to produce about 2 tablespoons of smooth juice.

3 Place the tamarind juice in a food processor with the shallots, garlic, ginger, coriander, chillies and turmeric. Blend until smooth, adding a little more hot water if necessary, and reserve the paste.

4 Heat a wok or large frying pan, add the oil and, when hot, stir–fry the duck in batches for about 3 minutes, or until just coloured, then drain on absorbent kitchen paper.

5 Discard all but 2 tablespoons of the oil in the wok. Return to the heat. Add the paste and stir–fry for 5 minutes. Add the duck and stir–fry for 2 minutes. Add the bamboo shoots and stir–fry for 2 minutes. Season to taste with salt and pepper. Turn into a warmed serving dish, garnish with a sprig of fresh coriander and serve immediately with rice.

Ingredients   SERVES 4

4 small boneless duck breasts, with skin on, thinly sliced on the diagonal
1 tsp salt
4 tbsp tamarind pulp
4 shallots, peeled and chopped
2 garlic cloves, peeled and chopped
2.5 cm/1 inch piece fresh root ginger, chopped
1 tsp ground coriander
3 large red chillies, deseeded and chopped
$^1/_2$ tsp turmeric
125 ml/4 fl oz vegetable oil
227 g can bamboo shoots, drained, rinsed and finely sliced
salt and freshly ground black pepper
sprigs of fresh coriander, to garnish
freshly cooked rice, to serve

Nutritional details per 100 g   energy 258 kcals/1078 kj • protein 10 g • carbohydrate 9 g • fat 20 g • fibre 0.1 g • sugar trace • sodium 0.2 g

✓ cow's milk-free   ✓ egg-free   ✓ gluten-free   ✓ wheat-free   ✓ nut-free   ● vegetarian   ● vegan   ✓ seafood-free

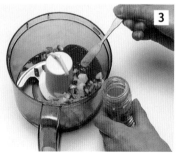

Hot & Spicy Red Cabbage with Apples

1 Preheat the oven to 150°C/300°F/Gas Mark 2. Put just enough cabbage in a large casserole to cover the base evenly.

2 Place a layer of the onions and apples on top of the cabbage.

3 Sprinkle a little of the mixed spice, cinnamon and sugar over the top. Season with salt and pepper.

4 Spoon over a small portion of the orange rind, orange juice and the cider.

5 Continue to layer the casserole with the ingredients in the same order until used up.

6 Pour the vinegar as evenly as possible over the top layer of the ingredients.

7 Cover the casserole with a close-fitting lid and bake in the preheated oven, stirring occasionally, for 2 hours until the cabbage is moist and tender. Serve immediately with the dairy-free yogurt and black pepper.

Ingredients   SERVES 8

900 g/2 lb red cabbage, cored
    and shredded
450 g/1 lb onions, peeled and
    finely sliced
450 g/1 lb cooking apples, peeled,
    cored and finely sliced
$\frac{1}{2}$ tsp mixed spice
1 tsp ground cinnamon
2 tbsp light soft brown sugar
salt and freshly ground black pepper
grated rind of 1 large orange
1 tbsp fresh orange juice
50 ml/2 fl oz medium sweet cider
    (or apple juice)
2 tbsp wine vinegar

To serve:

dairy-free yogurt
freshly ground black pepper

Nutritional details per 100 g   energy 42 kcals/176 kj • protein 1 g • carbohydrate 8 g • fat 0.6 g • fibre 0.4 g • sugar 5 g • sodium trace

✓ cow's milk-free   ✓ egg-free   ✓ gluten-free   ✓ wheat-free   ✓ nut-free   ✓ vegetarian   ◐ vegan   ✓ seafood-free

2

4

5

Meatballs with Bean & Tomato Sauce

1 Make the meatballs by blending half the onion, half the red pepper, the oregano, the paprika and 350 g/12 oz of the kidney beans in a blender or food processor for a few seconds. Add the beef with some seasoning and blend until well mixed. Turn the mixture onto a lightly floured board and form into small balls.

2 Heat the wok, then add 2 tablespoons of the oil and, when hot, stir-fry the meatballs gently until well browned on all sides. Remove with a slotted spoon and keep warm.

3 Wipe the wok clean, then add the remaining oil and cook the remaining onion and pepper and the garlic for 3–4 minutes, until soft. Add the tomatoes, seasoning to taste and remaining kidney beans.

4 Return the meatballs to the wok, stir them into the sauce, then cover and simmer for 10 minutes. Sprinkle with the chopped coriander and serve immediately with the freshly cooked rice.

Ingredients   SERVES 4

1 large onion, peeled and
   finely chopped
1 red pepper, deseeded
   and chopped
1 tbsp freshly chopped oregano
$^{1}/_{2}$ tsp hot paprika
425 g can red kidney beans, drained
300 g/11 oz fresh beef mince
salt and freshly ground black pepper
4 tbsp sunflower oil
1 garlic clove, peeled and crushed
400 g can chopped tomatoes
1 tbsp freshly chopped coriander,
   to garnish
freshly cooked rice, to serve

Nutritional details per 100 g   energy 112 kcals/471 kj • protein 6 g • carbohydrate 12 g • fat 5 g • fibre 2 g • sugar 3 g • sodium 0.1 g

✓ cow's milk-free   ✓ egg-free   ✓ gluten-free   ✓ wheat-free   ✓ nut-free   ○ vegetarian   ○ vegan   ✓ seafood-free

1

2

4

Mediterranean Rice Salad

1 Cook the rice in a saucepan of lightly salted boiling water for 35–40 minutes, or until tender. Drain well and reserve.

2 Whisk the sun-dried tomatoes, garlic, oil and vinegars together in a small bowl or jug. Season to taste with salt and pepper. Put the red onion in a large bowl, pour over the dressing and leave to allow the flavours to develop.

3 Put the peppers, skin-side up, on a grill rack and cook under a preheated hot grill for 5–6 minutes, or until blackened and charred. Remove and place in a plastic bag. When cool enough to handle, peel off the skins and slice the peppers.

4 Add the peppers, cucumber, tomatoes, fennel and rice to the onions. Mix gently together to coat in the dressing. Cover and chill in the refrigerator for 30 minutes to allow the flavours to mingle.

5 Remove the salad from the refrigerator and leave to stand at room temperature for 20 minutes. Garnish with fresh basil leaves and serve.

Ingredients   SERVES 4

250 g/9 oz Camargue red rice
2 sun-dried tomatoes,
   finely chopped
2 garlic cloves, peeled and
   finely chopped
4 tbsp oil from a jar of
   sun-dried tomatoes
2 tsp balsamic vinegar
2 tsp red wine vinegar
salt and freshly ground black pepper
1 red onion, peeled and thinly sliced
1 yellow pepper, quartered
   and deseeded
1 red pepper, quartered
   and deseeded
1/2 cucumber, peeled and diced
6 ripe plum tomatoes, cut
   into wedges
1 fennel bulb, halved and
   thinly sliced
fresh basil leaves, to garnish

Nutritional details per 100 g   energy 48 kcals/202 kj • protein 1 g • carbohydrate 9 g • fat 1 g • fibre trace • sugar trace • sodium trace

✓ cow's milk-free   ✓ egg-free   ✓ gluten-free   ✓ wheat-free   ✓ nut-free   ✓ vegetarian   ⦿ vegan   ✓ seafood-free

Oven-baked Pork Balls with Peppers

1 Preheat oven to 200°C/400°F/Gas Mark 6, 15 minutes before cooking.

2 Mix together the pork, basil, 1 chopped garlic clove, sun–dried tomatoes and seasoning until well combined.

3 With damp hands, divide the mixture into 16 equal portions, then roll into balls and reserve.

4 Spoon the olive oil into a large roasting tin and place in the preheated oven for about 3 minutes, until very hot.

5 Remove from the heat and stir in the pork balls, the remaining chopped garlic and peppers. Bake for about 15 minutes.

6 Remove from the oven and stir in the cherry tomatoes and season to taste with plenty of salt and pepper. Bake for about a further 20 minutes.

7 Remove the pork balls from the oven, stir in the vinegar and serve immediately.

Ingredients   SERVES 4

450 g/1 lb fresh pork mince

4 tbsp freshly chopped basil

2 garlic cloves, peeled and chopped

3 sun–dried tomatoes, chopped

salt and freshly ground black pepper

3 tbsp olive oil

1 medium red pepper, deseeded and
    cut into chunks

1 medium green pepper, deseeded
    and cut into chunks

1 medium yellow pepper, deseeded
    and cut into chunks

225 g/8 oz cherry tomatoes

2 tbsp balsamic vinegar

Nutritional details per 100 g   energy 139 kcals/582 kj • protein 8 g • carbohydrate 5 g • fat 10 g • fibre 0.5 g • sugar 1 g • sodium 0.2 g

✓ cow's milk-free   ✓ egg-free   ✓ gluten-free   ✓ wheat-free   ✓ nut-free   ● vegetarian   ● vegan   ✓ seafood-free

Pork Cabbage Parcels

1 Preheat the oven to 180°C/350°F/Gas Mark 4, 10 minutes before cooking. To make the sauce, heat the oil in a heavy-based saucepan, add the spring onions and cook for 2 minutes, or until softened.

2 Add the tomatoes and mint to the saucepan, bring to the boil, cover, then simmer for 10 minutes. Season to taste with pepper. Reheat when required.

3 Meanwhile, blanch the cabbage leaves in a large saucepan of lightly salted water for 3 minutes. Drain and refresh under cold running water. Pat dry with absorbent kitchen paper and reserve.

4 Heat the oil in a small saucepan, add the carrot and pork mince and cook for 3 minutes. Add the mushrooms and cook for 3 minutes. Stir in the Chinese five-spice powder, rice and lemon juice and heat through.

5 Place some of the filling in the centre of each cabbage leaf and fold to enclose the filling. Place in a shallow ovenproof dish seam-side down. Pour over the stock and cook in the preheated oven for 30 minutes. Serve immediately with the reheated tomato sauce.

Ingredients SERVES 4

8 large green cabbage leaves
1 tbsp vegetable oil
1 carrot, peeled and cut
    into matchsticks
125 g/4 oz fresh pork mince
50 g/2 oz button mushrooms,
    wiped and sliced
1 tsp Chinese five-spice powder
50 g/2 oz cooked long-grain rice
juice of 1 lemon
150 ml/¼ pint gluten-free
    chicken stock

For the tomato sauce:

1 tbsp vegetable oil
1 bunch spring onions,
    trimmed and chopped
400 g can chopped tomatoes
1 tbsp freshly chopped mint
freshly ground black pepper

Nutritional details per 100 g energy 126 kcals/524 kj • protein 7 g • carbohydrate 6 g • fat 9 g • fibre 0.7 g • sugar 1 g • sodium 0.1 g

✓ cow's milk-free ✓ egg-free ✓ gluten-free ✓ wheat-free ✓ nut-free ● vegetarian ● vegan ✓ seafood-free

Venetian Herb Orzo

1 Rinse the spinach leaves in several changes of cold water and reserve. Finely chop the rocket leaves with the parsley and mint. Thinly slice the green of the spring onions.

2 Bring a large saucepan of water to the boil, add the spinach leaves, herbs and spring onions and cook for about 10 seconds. Remove and rinse under cold running water. Drain well and, using your hands, squeeze out all the excess moisture.

3 Place the spinach, herbs and spring onions in a food processor. Blend for 1 minute then, with the motor running, gradually pour in the olive oil until the sauce is well blended.

4 Meanwhile, bring a large pan of lightly salted water to a rolling boil. Add the pasta and cook according to the packet instructions, or until 'al dente'. Drain thoroughly and place in a large warmed bowl.

5 Add the spinach sauce to the orzo and stir lightly until the orzo is well coated. Stir in an extra tablespoon of olive oil if the mixture seems too thick. Season well with salt and pepper. Serve immediately on warmed plates or allow to cool to room temperature.

Ingredients SERVES 4–6

200 g/7 oz baby spinach leaves
150 g/5 oz rocket leaves
50 g/2 oz flat leaf parsley
6 spring onions, trimmed
few leaves of fresh mint
3 tbsp extra virgin olive oil,
    plus more if required
450 g/11 oz orzo
salt and freshly ground black pepper

Nutritional details per 100 g energy 121 kcals/505 kj • protein 2 g • carbohydrate 17 g • fat 5 g • fibre 1 g • sugar 0.5 g • sodium trace

✓ cow's milk-free ✓ egg-free ● gluten-free ● wheat-free ✓ nut-free ✓ vegetarian ✓ vegan ✓ seafood-free

1

3

5

Warm Chicken & Potato Salad with Peas & Mint

1 Cook the potatoes in lightly salted boiling water for 15 minutes, or until just tender when pierced with the tip of a sharp knife; do not overcook. Rinse under cold running water to cool slightly, then drain and turn into a large bowl. Sprinkle with the cider vinegar and toss gently.

2 Run the peas under hot water to ensure that they are thawed, pat dry with absorbent kitchen paper and add to the potatoes.

3 Cut the avocado in half lengthways and remove the stone. Peel and cut the avocado into cubes and add to the potatoes and peas. Add the chicken and stir together lightly.

4 To make the dressing, place all the ingredients in a screw-top jar with a little salt and pepper and shake well to mix; add a little more oil if the flavour is too sharp. Pour over the salad and toss gently to coat. Sprinkle in half the mint and stir lightly.

5 Separate the lettuce leaves and spread onto a large shallow serving plate. Spoon the salad on top and sprinkle with the remaining mint. Garnish with mint sprigs and serve.

Ingredients   SERVES 4–6

450 g/1 lb new potatoes, peeled
  or scrubbed and cut into
  bite-sized pieces
salt and freshly ground black pepper
2 tbsp cider vinegar
175 g/6 oz frozen garden
  peas, thawed
1 small ripe avocado
4 cooked chicken breasts, about 450
  g/1 lb in weight, skinned and diced
2 tbsp freshly chopped mint
2 heads Little Gem lettuce
fresh mint sprigs, to garnish

For the dressing:

2 tbsp raspberry or sherry vinegar
2 tsp gluten-free Dijon mustard
1 tsp clear honey
50 ml/2 fl oz sunflower oil
50 ml/2 fl oz extra virgin olive oil

Nutritional details per 100 g energy 138 kcals/577 kj · protein 12 g · carbohydrate 8 g · fat 7 g · fibre 1 g · sugar 1 g · sodium trace

✓ cow's milk-free ✓ egg-free ✓ gluten-free ✓ wheat-free ✓ nut-free ● vegetarian ● vegan ✓ seafood-free

Wheat- & Gluten-free

Living with intolerance to wheat and gluten need not be difficult if you manage to replace this important complex carbohydrate with other fibre-rich foods. This section provides enticing recipes that avoid foods which contain wheat and gluten, and offer a healthy alternative.

Aubergine & Yogurt Dip

1 Preheat the oven to 200°C/400°F/Gas Mark 6. Pierce the skin of the aubergines with a fork and place on a baking tray. Cook for 40 minutes or until very soft.

2 Cool the aubergines, then cut in half, scoop out the flesh and tip into a bowl.

3 Mash the aubergine with the olive oil, lemon juice and garlic until smooth or blend for a few seconds in a food processor.

4 Chop the pimentos finely and add to the aubergine mixture.

5 When blended, add the yogurt. Stir well and season to taste with salt and pepper.

6 Add the chopped olives and leave in the refrigerator to chill for at least 30 minutes.

7 Place the cauliflower and broccoli florets and carrot strips into a pan and cover with boiling water. Simmer for 2 minutes, then rinse in cold water. Drain and serve as crudités to accompany the dip.

Ingredients

MAKES 600 ml/1 PINT

2 x 225 g/8 oz aubergines
1 tbsp light olive oil
1 tbsp lemon juice
2 garlic cloves, peeled and crushed
190 g jar pimentos, drained
150 ml/¼ pint low-fat
   natural yogurt
salt and freshly ground black pepper
25 g/1 oz black olives, pitted
   and chopped
225 g/8 oz cauliflower florets
225 g/8 oz broccoli florets
125 g/4 oz carrots, peeled and cut
   into 5 cm/2 inch strips

Nutritional details per 100 g energy 36 kcals/150 kj • protein 2 g • carbohydrate 5 g • fat 1 g • fibre 0.7 g • sugar 1.4 g • sodium trace
cow's milk-free ✔ egg-free ✔ gluten-free ✔ wheat-free ✔ nut-free ✔ vegetarian vegan ✔ seafood-free

1

3

4

Baby Roast Potato Salad

1 Preheat the oven to 200°C/400°F/Gas Mark 6. Trim the shallots, but leave the skins on. Put into a saucepan of lightly salted boiling water along with the potatoes and cook for 5 minutes and drain. Separate the shallots and plunge them into cold water for 1 minute.

2 Put the oil on a baking sheet lined with foil or roasting tin and heat for a few minutes. Peel the skins off the shallots – they should now come away easily. Add to the baking sheet or roasting tin with the potatoes and toss in the oil to coat. Sprinkle with a little sea salt. Roast the potatoes and shallots in the preheated oven for 10 minutes.

3 Meanwhile, trim the courgettes, halve lengthways and cut into 5 cm/2 inch chunks. Add to the baking sheet or roasting tin, toss to mix and cook for 5 minutes.

4 Pierce the tomato skins with a sharp knife. Add to the sheet or tin with the rosemary and cook for a further 5 minutes, or until all the vegetables are tender. Remove the rosemary and discard. Grind a little black pepper over the vegetables.

5 Spoon into a wide serving bowl. Mix together the soured cream, paprika and chives and drizzle over the vegetables just before serving.

Ingredients   SERVES 4

350 g/12 oz small shallots
sea salt and freshly ground
    black pepper
900 g/2 lb small, even–sized
    new potatoes
2 tbsp olive oil
2 medium courgettes
2 sprigs of fresh rosemary
175 g/6 oz cherry tomatoes
150 ml/$^1/_4$ pint soured cream
2 tbsp freshly snipped chives
$^1/_4$ tsp paprika

Nutritional details per 100 g energy 68 kcals/286 kj • protein 2 g • carbohydrate 9 g • fat 3 g • fibre 1.1 g • sugar 1.6 g • sodium trace

cow's milk-free   ✓ egg-free   ✓ gluten-free   ✓ wheat-free   ✓ nut-free   ✓ vegetarian   vegan   ✓ seafood-free

Carrot & Parsnip Terrine

1. Preheat the oven to 200 C/400 F/Gas Mark 6. Oil and line a 900 g/2 lb loaf tin with non-stick baking paper. Cook the carrots and parsnips in boiling salted water for 10–15 minutes or until very tender. Drain and purée separately. Add 2 tablespoons of crème fraîche to both the carrots and the parsnips. Steam the spinach for 5–10 minutes or until very tender. Drain and squeeze out as much liquid as possible, then stir in the remaining crème fraîche. Add the brown sugar to the carrot purée, the parsley to the parsnip mixture and the nutmeg to the spinach. Season all three to taste with salt and pepper.

2. Beat 2 eggs, add to the spinach and turn into the tin. Add another 2 beaten eggs to the carrot mixture and layer carefully on top. Beat the remaining eggs into the parsnip purée and layer on top. Place the tin in a baking dish and pour in enough hot water to come halfway up the sides of the tin. Bake for 1 hour until a skewer inserted into the centre comes out clean. Leave to cool for at least 30 minutes. Run a sharp knife around the edges. Turn out on to a dish and reserve.

3. Make the tomato coulis by simmering the tomatoes and onions together for 5–10 minutes until slightly thickened. Season to taste. Blend well in a liquidiser or food processor and serve as an accompaniment. Garnish with sprigs of basil and serve.

Ingredients   SERVES 8–10

550 g/1¼ lb carrots, peeled and chopped
450 g/1 lb parsnips, peeled and chopped
6 tbsp half-fat crème fraîche
450 g/1 lb spinach, rinsed
1 tbsp brown sugar
1 tbsp freshly chopped parsley
½ tsp freshly grated nutmeg
salt and freshly ground black pepper
6 medium eggs
sprigs of fresh basil, to garnish

For the tomato coulis:

450 g/1 lb ripe tomatoes, deseeded and chopped
1 medium onion, peeled and finely chopped

Nutritional details per 100 g   energy 49 kcals/206 kj • protein 3 g • carbohydrate 6 g • fat 2 g • fibre 2.2 g • sugar 4.2 g • sodium trace
cow's milk-free   egg-free   ✓ gluten-free   ✓ wheat-free   ✓ nut-free   ✓ vegetarian   vegan   ✓ seafood-free

Chicken & Seafood Risotto

1. Heat half the oil in a 45.5 cm/18 inch paella pan or deep, wide frying pan. Add the chicken pieces and fry for 15 minutes, turning constantly, until golden. Remove from the pan and reserve. Add the chorizo and ham to the pan and cook for 6 minutes until crisp, stirring occasionally. Remove and add to the chicken.

2. Add the onion to the pan and cook for 3 minutes until beginning to soften. Add the peppers and garlic and cook for 2 minutes, then add to the reserved chicken, chorizo and ham.

3. Add the remaining oil to the pan and stir in the rice until well coated. Stir in the bay leaves, thyme and saffron, then pour in the wine and bubble until evaporated, stirring and scraping up any bits on the bottom of the pan. Stir in the stock and bring to the boil, stirring occasionally.

4. Return the chicken, chorizo, ham and vegetables to the pan, burying them gently in the rice. Season to taste with salt and pepper. Reduce the heat and simmer for 10 minutes, stirring occasionally.

5. Add the peas and seafood, pushing them gently into the rice. Cover, cook over a low heat for 5 minutes, or until the rice and prawns are tender and the clams and mussels open – discard any that do not open. Stand for 5 minutes. Sprinkle with the parsley and serve.

Ingredients   SERVES 6–9

125 ml/4 fl oz olive oil

1.4 kg/3 lb chicken, cut into 8 pieces

350 g/12 oz spicy chorizo sausage, cut into 1 cm/$^1/_2$ inch pieces

125 g/4 oz cured ham, diced

1 onion, peeled and chopped

2 red or yellow peppers, deseeded and cut into 2.5 cm/1 inch pieces

4 garlic cloves, peeled and finely chopped

750 g/1 lb 10 oz short–grain Spanish rice or Arborio rice

2 bay leaves

1 tsp dried thyme

1 tsp saffron strands, lightly crushed

200 ml/7 fl oz dry white wine

1.6 litres/2$^3/_4$ pints gluten–free chicken stock

salt and freshly ground black pepper

125 g/4 oz freshly shelled peas

450 g/1 lb uncooked prawns

36 clams and/or mussels, well scrubbed

2 tbsp freshly chopped parsley

fresh parsley sprigs, to garnish

Nutritional details per 100 g   energy 152 kcals/638 kj • protein 17 g • carbohydrate 7 g • fat 6 g • fibre 0.3 g • sugar 0.8 g • sodium 0.5 g

✓ cow's milk–free   ✓ egg–free   ✓ gluten–free   ✓ wheat–free   ✓ nut–free   ◐ vegetarian   ◐ vegan   ◐ seafood–free

Coconut Seafood

1. Heat a large wok, add the oil and heat until it is almost smoking, swirling the oil around the wok to coat the sides. Add the prawns and stir-fry over a high heat for 4–5 minutes, or until browned on all sides. Using a slotted spoon, transfer the prawns to a plate and keep warm in a low oven.

2. Add the spring onions, garlic and ginger to the wok and stir-fry for 1 minute. Add the mushrooms and stir-fry for a further 3 minutes. Using a slotted spoon, transfer the mushroom mixture to a plate and keep warm in a low oven.

3. Add the wine and coconut cream to the wok, bring to the boil and boil rapidly for 4 minutes, until reduced slightly.

4. Return the mushroom mixture and prawns to the wok, bring back to the boil, then simmer for 1 minute, stirring occasionally, until piping hot. Stir in the freshly chopped coriander and season to taste with salt and pepper. Serve immediately with the freshly cooked fragrant Thai rice.

Ingredients   SERVES 4

2 tbsp sunflower oil
450 g/1 lb raw king prawns, peeled
2 bunches spring onions, trimmed
  and thickly sliced
1 garlic clove, peeled and chopped
2.5 cm/1 inch piece fresh
  root ginger, peeled and cut
  into matchsticks
125 g/4 oz fresh shiitake
  mushrooms, rinsed and halved
150 ml/¹/₄ pint dry white wine
200 ml/7 fl oz carton coconut cream
4 tbsp coriander, freshly chopped
salt and freshly ground black pepper
freshly cooked fragrant Thai rice,
  to serve

Nutritional details per 100 g   energy 125 kcals/527 kj · protein 8 g · carbohydrate 12 g · fat 5 g · fibre 0.2 g · sugar 0.3 g · sodium 0.5 g

✓ cow's milk-free   ✓ egg-free   ✓ gluten-free   ✓ wheat-free   ✓ nut-free   ● vegetarian   ● vegan   ● seafood-free

Crown Roast of Lamb

1 Preheat the oven to 180°C/350°F/Gas Mark 4, about 10 minutes before roasting. Wipe the crown roast and season the cavity with salt and pepper. Place in a roasting tin and cover the ends of the bones with small pieces of foil.

2 Heat the oil in a small saucepan and cook the onion, garlic and celery for 5 minutes, then remove the saucepan from the heat. Add the cooked rice with the apricots, pine nuts, orange rind and coriander. Season with salt and pepper, then stir in the egg and mix well.

3 Carefully spoon the prepared stuffing into the cavity of the lamb, then roast in the preheated oven for 1–1¹/₂ hours. Remove the lamb from the oven and remove and discard the foil from the bones. Return to the oven and continue to cook for a further 15 minutes, or until cooked to personal preference.

4 Remove from the oven and leave to rest for 10 minutes before serving with the roast potatoes and freshly cooked vegetables.

Ingredients   SERVES 6

1 lamb crown roast
salt and freshly ground black pepper
1 tbsp sunflower oil
1 small onion, peeled and
    finely chopped
2–3 garlic cloves, peeled and crushed
2 celery stalks, trimmed and
    finely chopped
125 g/4 oz cooked mixed basmati
    and wild rice
75 g/3 oz ready-to-eat dried
    apricots, chopped
50 g/2 oz pine nuts, toasted
1 tbsp finely grated orange rind
2 tbsp freshly chopped coriander
1 small egg, beaten
freshly roasted potatoes and green
    vegetables, to serve

Nutritional details per 100 g energy 147 kcals/617 kj • protein 6 g • carbohydrate 17 g • fat 7 g • fibre 2 g • sugar 2.7 g • sodium trace

✓ cow's milk-free   egg-free   ✓ gluten-free   ✓ wheat-free   nut-free   vegetarian   vegan   ✓ seafood-free

Fragrant Fruit Pilaf

1 Melt half the butter in a saucepan or casserole with a tight-fitting lid. Add the cardamom pods and cinnamon stick and cook for about 30 seconds before adding the bay leaves and rice. Stir well to coat the rice in the butter and add the stock. Bring to the boil, cover tightly and cook very gently for 15 minutes. Remove from the heat and leave to stand for a further 5 minutes.

2 Melt the remaining butter in a wok and, when foaming, add the onion, flaked almonds and pistachios. Stir-fry for 3–4 minutes until the nuts are beginning to brown. Remove and reserve.

3 Reduce the heat slightly and add the dried figs, apricots and chicken and continue stir-frying for a further 7–8 minutes until the chicken is cooked through. Add the nut mixture and toss to mix.

4 Remove from the heat, then remove the cinnamon stick and bay leaves. Add the cooked rice and stir together well to mix. Season to taste with salt and pepper. Garnish with parsley or coriander leaves and serve immediately.

Ingredients SERVES 4-6

50 g/2 oz butter
6 green cardamom pods
1 cinnamon stick
2 bay leaves
450 g/1 lb basmati rice
600 ml/1 pint gluten-free
 chicken stock
1 onion, peeled and finely chopped
50 g/2 oz flaked almonds
50 g/2 oz shelled pistachios,
 roughly chopped
125 g/4 oz ready-to-eat dried figs,
 roughly chopped
50 g/2 oz ready-to-eat dried
 apricots, roughly chopped
275 g/10 oz skinless chicken breast
 fillets, cut into chunks
salt and freshly ground black pepper
fresh parsley or coriander leaves,
 to garnish

Nutritional details per 100 g energy 197 kcals/825 kj • protein 10 g • carbohydrate 20 g • fat 8 g • fibre 1.2 g • sugar 7.7 g • sodium 0.2 g

cow's milk-free ✓ egg-free ✓ gluten-free ✓ wheat-free nut-free vegetarian vegan ✓ seafood-free

Fresh Tuna Salad

1 Wash the salad leaves and place in a large salad bowl with the cherry tomatoes and rocket and reserve.

2 Heat the wok, then add the oil and heat until almost smoking. Add the tuna, skin–side down, and cook for 4–6 minutes, turning once during cooking, or until cooked and the flesh flakes easily. Remove from the heat and leave to stand in the juices for 2 minutes before removing.

3 Meanwhile, make the dressing. Place the olive oil, lemon zest and juices and mustard in a small bowl or screw–top jar and whisk or shake until well blended. Season to taste with salt and pepper.

4 Transfer the tuna to a clean chopping board and flake, then add it to the salad and toss lightly.

5 Using a swivel blade vegetable peeler, peel the piece of Parmesan cheese into shavings. Divide the salad between four large serving plates, drizzle the dressing over the salad, then scatter with the Parmesan shavings.

Ingredients   SERVES 4

225 g/8 oz mixed salad leaves
225 g/8 oz baby cherry tomatoes, halved lengthways
125 g/4 oz rocket leaves, washed
2 tbsp olive oil
550 g/1¼ lb boned tuna steaks, each cut into 4 small pieces
50 g/2 oz piece fresh Parmesan cheese

For the dressing:

8 tbsp olive oil
juice and grated zest of 2 small lemons
1 tbsp gluten–free wholegrain mustard
salt and freshly ground black pepper

Nutritional details per 100 g   energy 156 kcals/646 kj • protein 13 g • carbohydrate 3 g • fat 8 g • fibre 0.1 g • sugar 0.2 g • sodium trace

○ cow's milk-free   ✓ egg-free   ✓ gluten-free   ✓ wheat-free   ✓ nut-free   ○ vegetarian   ○ vegan   ○ seafood-free

Hot-&-Sour Mushroom Soup

1 Heat the oil in a frying pan, add the garlic and shallots and cook until golden brown and starting to crisp. Remove from the pan and reserve. Add the chillies to the pan and cook until they start to change colour.

2 Place the garlic, shallots and chillies in a food processor or blender and blend to a smooth purée with 150 ml/¼ pint water. Pour the purée back into the pan, add the sugar with a large pinch of salt, then cook gently, stirring, until dark in colour. Take care not to burn the mixture.

3 Pour the stock into a large saucepan and add the garlic purée, rice, lime leaves and the lemon rind and juice. Bring to the boil, then reduce the heat, cover and simmer gently for about 10 minutes.

4 Add the mushrooms and simmer for a further 10 minutes, or until the mushrooms and rice are tender. Remove the lime leaves, stir in the chopped coriander and ladle into bowls. Place the chopped green chillies and spring onions in small bowls and serve separately to sprinkle on top of the soup.

Ingredients   SERVES 4

4 tbsp sunflower oil
3 garlic cloves, peeled and
    finely chopped
3 shallots, peeled and finely chopped
2 large red chillies, deseeded and
    finely chopped
1 tbsp soft brown sugar
large pinch of salt
1 litre/1¾ pints gluten–free
    vegetable stock
250 g/9 oz Thai fragrant rice
5 kaffir lime leaves, torn
juice and grated rind of 1 lemon
250 g/9 oz oyster mushrooms, wiped
    and cut into pieces
2 tbsp freshly chopped coriander

To garnish:

2 green chillies, deseeded and
    finely chopped
3 spring onions, trimmed and
    finely chopped

Nutritional details per 100 g   energy 110 kcals/458 kj • protein 3 g • carbohydrate 14 g • fat 5 g • fibre 0.2 g • sugar 2.6 g • sodium 0.3 g

✓ cow's milk-free   ✓ egg-free   ✓ gluten–free   ✓ wheat-free   ✓ nut-free   ✓ vegetarian   ✓ vegan   ✓ seafood-free

1

2

4

Pumpkin & Smoked Haddock Soup

1   Heat the oil in a large heavy-based saucepan and gently cook the onion, garlic and celery for about 10 minutes. This will release the sweetness but not colour the vegetables. Add the pumpkin and potatoes to the saucepan and stir to coat the vegetables with the oil.

2   Gradually pour in the stock and bring to the boil. Cover, then reduce the heat and simmer for 25 minutes, stirring occasionally. Stir in the dry sherry, then remove the saucepan from the heat and leave to cool for 5–10 minutes.

3   Blend the mixture in a food processor or blender to form a chunky purée and return to the saucepan.

4   Meanwhile, place the fish in a shallow frying pan. Pour in the milk with 3 tablespoons of water and bring to almost boiling point. Reduce the heat, cover and simmer for 6 minutes, or until the fish is cooked and flakes easily. Remove from the heat and, using a slotted spoon, remove the fish from the liquid, reserving both liquid and fish.

5   Discard the skin and any bones from the fish and flake into pieces. Stir the fish liquid into the soup, together with the flaked fish. Season with freshly ground black pepper, stir in the parsley and serve immediately.

Ingredients   SERVES 4–6

2 tbsp olive oil
1 medium onion, peeled and chopped
2 garlic cloves, peeled and chopped
3 celery stalks, trimmed and chopped
700 g/1 1/2 lb pumpkin, peeled, deseeded and cut into chunks
450 g/1 lb potatoes, peeled and cut into chunks
750 ml/1 1/4 pints gluten-free chicken stock, heated
125 ml/4 fl oz dry sherry
200 g/7 oz smoked haddock fillet
150 ml/1/4 pint milk
freshly ground black pepper
2 tbsp freshly chopped parsley

Nutritional details per 100 g   energy 58 kcals/246 kj • protein 4 g • carbohydrate 6 g • fat 1.7 g • fibre 0.9 g • sugar 1.8 g • sodium 0.3 g
⬤ cow's milk-free   ✓ egg-free   ✓ gluten-free   ✓ wheat-free   ✓ nut-free   ⬤ vegetarian   ⬤ vegan   ⬤ seafood-free

1

4

5

Seared Scallop Salad

1   Clean the scallops, removing the thin black vein from around the white meat and coral. Rinse thoroughly and dry on absorbent kitchen paper.

2   Cut into 2–3 thick slices, depending on the scallop size.

3   Heat a griddle pan or heavy–based frying pan, then, when hot, add the butter and allow to melt.

4   Once melted, sear the scallops for 1 minute on each side or until golden. Remove from the pan and reserve.

5   Briskly whisk together the orange juice, balsamic vinegar and honey to make the dressing and reserve.

6   With a small, sharp knife, carefully cut the pears into quarters, core then cut into chunks.

7   Mix the rocket leaves, watercress, pear chunks and walnuts. Pile onto serving plates and top with the scallops.

8   Drizzle over the dressing and grind over plenty of black pepper. Serve immediately.

Ingredients   SERVES 4

12 king (large) scallops
1 tbsp butter
2 tbsp orange juice
2 tbsp balsamic vinegar
1 tbsp clear honey
2 ripe pears, washed
125 g/4 oz rocket
125 g/4 oz watercress
50 g/2 oz walnuts
freshly ground black pepper

Nutritional details per 100 g energy 116 kcals/483 kj • protein 6 g • carbohydrate 8 g • fat 6 g • fibre 1.4 g • sugar 6.1 g • sodium 0.1 g

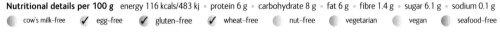

cow's milk-free   ✓ egg-free   ✓ gluten-free   ✓ wheat-free   nut-free   vegetarian   vegan   seafood-free

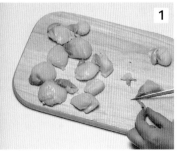

1

4

6

Special Rösti

1 Cook the potatoes in a large saucepan of salted boiling water for about 10 minutes, until just tender. Drain in a colander, then rinse in cold water. Drain again. Leave until cool enough to handle, then peel off the skins.

2 Melt the butter in a large frying pan and gently fry the onion and garlic for about 3 minutes until softened and beginning to colour. Remove from the heat.

3 Coarsely grate the potatoes into a large bowl, then stir in the onion and garlic mixture. Sprinkle over the parsley and stir well to mix. Season to taste with salt and pepper.

4 Heat the oil in the frying pan and cover the base of the pan with half the potato mixture. Lay the slices of Parma ham on top. Sprinkle with the chopped sun–dried tomatoes, then scatter the grated Emmenthal over the top.

5 Finally, top with the remaining potato mixture. Cook over a low heat, pressing down with a palette knife from time to time, for 10–15 minutes, or until the bottom is golden brown. Carefully invert the rösti onto a large plate, then carefully slide back into the pan and cook the other side until golden. Serve cut into wedges with a mixed green salad.

Ingredients   SERVES 4

700 g/1½ lb potatoes,
    scrubbed but not peeled
salt and freshly ground black pepper
75 g/3 oz butter
1 large onion, peeled and
    finely chopped
1 garlic clove, peeled and crushed
2 tbsp freshly chopped parsley
1 tbsp olive oil
75 g/3 oz Parma ham, thinly sliced
50 g/2 oz sun–dried tomatoes,
    chopped
175 g/6 oz Emmenthal
    cheese, grated
mixed green salad, to serve

Nutritional details per 100 g   energy 147 kcals/611 kj ● protein 5 g ● carbohydrate 11 g ● fat 9 g ● fibre 0.9 g ● sugar 1.5 g ● sodium 0.2 g

cow's milk-free   ✓ egg-free   ✓ gluten-free   ✓ wheat-free   ✓ nut-free   vegetarian   vegan   ✓ seafood-free

Spiced Indian Roast Potatoes with Chicken

1 Preheat the oven to 190°C/375°F/Gas Mark 5, about 10 minutes before cooking. Parboil the potatoes for 5 minutes in lightly salted boiling water, then drain thoroughly and reserve. Heat the oil in a large frying pan, add the chicken drumsticks and cook until sealed on all sides. Remove and reserve.

2 Add the onions and shallots to the pan and fry for 4–5 minutes, or until softened. Stir in the garlic, chilli and ginger and cook for 1 minute, stirring constantly. Stir in the ground cumin, coriander, cayenne pepper and crushed cardamom pods and continue to cook, stirring, for a further minute.

3 Add the potatoes to the pan, then add the chicken. Season to taste with salt and pepper. Stir gently until the potatoes and chicken pieces are coated in the onion and spice mixture.

4 Spoon into a large roasting tin and roast in the preheated oven for 35 minutes, or until the chicken and potatoes are cooked thoroughly. Garnish with fresh coriander and serve immediately.

Ingredients　　　SERVES 4

700 g/1½ lb waxy potatoes, peeled
　　and cut into large chunks
salt and freshly ground black pepper
4 tbsp sunflower oil
8 chicken drumsticks
1 large Spanish onion, peeled
　　and roughly chopped
3 shallots, peeled and roughly
　　chopped
2 large garlic cloves, peeled
　　and crushed
1 red chilli
2 tsp fresh root ginger, peeled
　　and finely grated
2 tsp ground cumin
2 tsp ground coriander
pinch of cayenne pepper
4 cardamom pods, crushed
sprigs of fresh coriander, to garnish

Nutritional details per 100 g　energy 142 kcals/598 kj　•　protein 9 g　•　carbohydrate 14 g　•　fat 5 g　•　fibre 1.2 g　•　sugar 1.3 g　•　sodium trace

✓ cow's milk-free　　✓ egg-free　　✓ gluten-free　　✓ wheat-free　　✓ nut-free　　● vegetarian　　● vegan　　✓ seafood-free

Almond Macaroons

1 Preheat the oven to 150°C/300°F/Gas Mark 2, 10 minutes before baking. Line a baking sheet with the rice paper.

2 Mix the caster sugar, ground almonds, ground rice and almond essence together and reserve.

3 Whisk the egg white until stiff then gently fold in the caster sugar mixture with a metal spoon or rubber spatula.

4 Mix to form a stiff, but not sticky, paste. If the mixture is very sticky, add a little extra ground almonds.

5 Place small spoonfuls of the mixture, about the size of an apricot, well apart on the rice paper.

6 Place a half–blanched almond in the centre of each. Place in the preheated oven and bake for 25 minutes, or until just pale golden.

7 Remove the biscuits from the oven and leave to cool for a few minutes on the baking sheet. Cut or tear the rice paper around the macaroons to release them. Once cold, serve or otherwise store them in an airtight tin.

Ingredients MAKES 12

rice paper
125 g/4 oz caster sugar
50 g/2 oz ground almonds
1 tsp ground rice
2–3 drops almond essence
1 medium egg white
8 blanched almonds, halved

Nutritional details per 100 g energy 383 kcals/1621 kj • protein 5 g • carbohydrate 72 g • fat 10 g • fibre trace • sugar 58 g • sodium trace

✓ cow's milk-free ◉ egg-free ✓ gluten–free ✓ wheat-free ◉ nut-free ✓ vegetarian ◉ vegan ✓ seafood-free

2

4

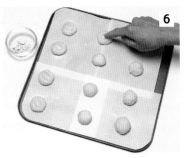

6

Chocolate Florentines

1 Preheat the oven to 180°C/350°F/Gas Mark 4, 10 minutes before baking. Lightly oil a baking sheet.

2 Melt the butter or margarine with the sugar and double cream in a small saucepan over a very low heat. Do not boil. Remove from the heat and stir in the almonds, hazelnuts, sultanas and cherries.

3 Drop teaspoonfuls of the mixture onto the baking sheet. Transfer to the preheated oven and bake for 10 minutes, until golden.

4 Leave the biscuits to cool on the baking sheet for about 5 minutes, then carefully transfer to a wire rack to cool.

5 Melt the plain, milk and white chocolates in separate bowls, either in the microwave following the manufacturer's instructions or in a small bowl, placed over a saucepan of gently simmering water.

6 Spread one third of the biscuits with the plain chocolate, one third with the milk chocolate and one third with the white chocolate. Mark out wavy lines on the chocolate when almost set with the tines of a fork. Alternatively, dip some of the biscuits in chocolate to half coat and serve.

Ingredients MAKES 20

125 g/4 oz butter or margarine
125 g/4 oz soft light brown sugar
1 tbsp double cream
50 g/2 oz blanched almonds, roughly chopped
50 g/2 oz hazelnuts, roughly chopped
75 g/3 oz sultanas
50 g/2 oz glacé cherries, roughly chopped
50 g/2 oz plain, dark chocolate, roughly chopped or broken
50 g/2 oz milk chocolate, roughly chopped or broken
50 g/2 oz white chocolate, roughly chopped or broken

Nutritional details per 100 g energy 502 kcals/2098 kj • protein 5 g • carbohydrate 50 g • fat 34 g • fibre 0.6 g • sugar 47 g • sodium 0.1 g

● cow's milk-free   ✓ egg-free   ✓ gluten-free   ✓ wheat-free   ● nut-free   ✓ vegetarian   ● vegan   ✓ seafood-free

Chocolate Mousse Cake

1   Preheat the oven to 180°C/350°F/Gas Mark 4, 10 minutes before baking. Lightly oil and line the bases of two 20.5 cm/8 inch springform tins with baking paper. Melt the chocolate and butter in a bowl over a saucepan of simmering water. Stir until smooth. Remove from the heat and stir in the brandy. Whisk the egg yolks and the sugar, reserving 2 tablespoons of the sugar, until thick and creamy. Slowly beat in the chocolate mixture until smooth. Whisk the egg whites until soft peaks form, then sprinkle over the sugar and continue whisking until stiff but not dry. Fold a large spoonful of the whites into the chocolate mixture. Gently fold in the remaining whites. Divide about two thirds of the mixture between the tins. Reserve the remaining one third of the mixture for the filling. Bake for about 20 minutes, or until well risen and set. Remove and cool for at least 1 hour. Loosen the edges of the cakes from the tins with a knife and lightly press the crusty edges down. Pour the rest of the mousse over one layer, spreading until even. Remove the other cake from the tin and gently invert on to the mousse, bottom side up to make a flat top layer. Discard the paper and chill for 4–6 hours until set.

2   Melt the cream and chocolate with the brandy in a saucepan and stir until smooth. Cool until thickened. Unclip the side of the mousse cake and place on a rack. Pour over half the glaze and spread. Let set, then decorate with curls and the remaining glaze.

Ingredients
CUTS INTO 8–10 SERVINGS

For the cake:
450 g/1 lb plain dark chocolate, chopped
125 g/4 oz butter, softened
3 tbsp brandy
9 large eggs, separated
150 g/5 oz caster sugar

For the chocolate glaze:
225 ml/8 fl oz double cream
225 g/8 oz plain dark chocolate, chopped
2 tbsp brandy
1 tbsp single cream and white chocolate curls, to decorate

Nutritional details per 100 g   energy 407 kcals/1699 kj • protein 6 g • carbohydrate 36 g • fat 26 g • fibre 1 g • sugar 35 g • sodium trace

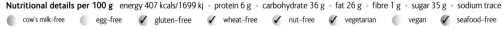

   cow's milk-free   egg-free   ✔ gluten-free   ✔ wheat-free   ✔ nut-free   ✔ vegetarian   vegan   ✔ seafood-free

Coconut Sorbet with Mango Sauce

1   Set the freezer to rapid freeze 2 hours before freezing the sorbet. Place the sheets of gelatine in a shallow dish, pour over cold water to cover and leave for 15 minutes. Squeeze out any excess moisture before use.

2   Meanwhile, place the caster sugar and 300 ml/^{1}/$_2$ pint of the coconut milk in a heavy–based saucepan and heat gently, stirring occasionally, until the sugar has dissolved. Remove from the heat. Add the soaked gelatine to the saucepan and stir gently until dissolved. Stir in the remaining coconut milk. Leave until cold.

3   Pour the gelatine and coconut mixture into a freezable container and place in the freezer. Leave for at least 1 hour, or until the mixture has started to form ice crystals. Remove and beat with a spoon, then return to the freezer and continue to freeze until the mixture is frozen, beating at least twice more during this time.

4   Meanwhile, make the sauce. Place the sliced mango, icing sugar and the lime zest and juice in a food processor and blend until smooth. Spoon into a small jug.

5   Leave the sorbet to soften in the refrigerator for at least 30 minutes before serving. Remember to turn the freezer to its normal setting.

Ingredients   SERVES 4

2 sheets gelatine
250 g/9 oz caster sugar
600 ml/1 pint coconut milk
2 mangos, peeled, pitted and sliced
2 tbsp icing sugar
zest and juice of 1 lime

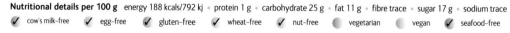

Nutritional details per 100 g   energy 188 kcals/792 kj • protein 1 g • carbohydrate 25 g • fat 11 g • fibre trace • sugar 17 g • sodium trace

✓ cow's milk-free   ✓ egg-free   ✓ gluten-free   ✓ wheat-free   ✓ nut-free   ◐ vegetarian   ◐ vegan   ✓ seafood-free

Dairy-free

Dairy foods can contain a high amount of cholesterol and saturated fat. Eating foods that avoid dairy is not just for those who are lactose intolerant but those wishing to follow a healthier lifestyle. The meals in this section offer nutritious and delicious alternatives to meals that include dairy, which will help you to lead such a lifestyle.

Aromatic Duck Burgers on Potato Pancakes

1 Peel off the thick layer of fat from the duck breasts and cut into small pieces. Put the fat into a small dry saucepan and set over a low heat for 10–15 minutes, or until the fat runs clear.

2 Cut the duck meat into pieces and blend in a food processor until coarsely chopped. Spoon into a bowl and add the hoisin sauce, garlic, half the spring onions, soy sauce and Chinese five-spice powder. Season to taste with salt and pepper and shape into four burgers. Cover and chill in the refrigerator for 1 hour.

3 Grate the potatoes into a large bowl, squeeze out the water with your hands, then put on a clean tea towel and twist the ends to squeeze out any remaining water. Return the potato to the bowl, add the onion and egg and mix well. Add the flour and salt and pepper. Stir to blend. Heat 2 tablespoons of the duck fat in a large frying pan. Spoon the potato into 2–4 pattie shapes and cook for 6 minutes, or until golden and crisp, turning once. Keep warm in the oven. Repeat with the remaining mixture, adding fat as needed.

4 Preheat the grill and line the rack with foil. Brush the burgers with a little of the duck fat and grill for 6–8 minutes, or longer if wished, turning once. Arrange 1–2 potato pancakes on a plate and top with a burger. Spoon over a little hoisin sauce and garnish with the remaining spring onions and coriander.

Ingredients SERVES 4

700 g/1½ lb boneless duck breasts
2 tbsp hoisin sauce
1 garlic clove, peeled and
    finely chopped
4 spring onions, trimmed and
    finely chopped
2 tbsp Japanese soy sauce
½ tsp Chinese five–spice powder
salt and freshly ground black pepper
freshly chopped coriander, to garnish
extra hoisin sauce, to serve

For the potato pancakes:

450 g/1 lb floury potatoes
1 small onion, peeled and grated
1 small egg, beaten
1 heaped tbsp plain flour

Nutritional details per 100 g energy 162 kcals/677 kj • protein 15 g • carbohydrate 7 g • fat 8 g • fibre 0.2 g • sugar 0.5 g • sodium 0.4 g

✓ cow's milk-free   egg-free   gluten-free   wheat-free   ✓ nut-free   vegetarian   vegan   ✓ seafood-free

Barbecued Fish Kebabs

1 Line a grill rack with a single layer of foil and preheat the grill at a high temperature, 2 minutes before use.

2 If using wooden skewers, soak in cold water for 30 minutes to prevent them from catching light during cooking.

3 Meanwhile, prepare the sauce. Add the fish stock, tomato ketchup, Worcestershire sauce, vinegar, sugar, Tabasco and tomato purée to a small saucepan. Stir well and leave to simmer for 5 minutes.

4 When ready to cook, drain the skewers, if necessary, then thread the fish chunks, the quartered red onions and the cherry tomatoes alternately on to the skewers.

5 Season the kebabs to taste with salt and pepper and brush with the sauce. Grill under the preheated grill for 8–10 minutes, basting with the sauce occasionally during cooking. Turn the kebabs often to ensure that they are cooked thoroughly and evenly on all sides. Serve immediately with couscous.

Ingredients   SERVES 4

450 g/1 lb herring or mackerel fillets,
  cut into chunks
2 small red onions, quartered
16 cherry tomatoes
salt and freshly ground black pepper
freshly cooked couscous, to serve

For the sauce:

150 ml/¹/₄ pint fish stock
5 tbsp tomato ketchup
2 tbsp Worcestershire sauce
2 tbsp wine vinegar
2 tbsp brown sugar
2 drops Tabasco
2 tbsp tomato purée

Nutritional details per 100 g   energy 116 kcals/486 kj • protein 9 g • carbohydrate 9 g • fat 5 g • fibre 0.3 g • sugar 7.4 g • sodium 0.3 g

✓ cow's milk-free   ✓ egg-free   ◑ gluten-free   ◑ wheat-free   ✓ nut-free   ◑ vegetarian   ◑ vegan   ◑ seafood-free

3

4

5

Braised Chicken in Beer

1 Preheat the oven to 170°C/325°F/Gas Mark 3. Cut each chicken joint in half and put in an ovenproof casserole with the prunes and bay leaves.

2 To peel the shallots, put in a small bowl and cover with boiling water. Drain the shallots after 2 minutes and rinse under cold water until cool enough to handle. The skins should then peel away easily from the shallots.

3 Heat the oil in a large, non-stick frying pan. Add the shallots and cook gently for about 5 minutes until beginning to colour. Add the mushrooms to the pan and cook for a further 3–4 minutes until both the mushrooms and onions are softened.

4 Sprinkle the sugar over the shallots and mushrooms, then add the mustard, tomato purée, ale and chicken stock. Season to taste with salt and pepper and bring to the boil, stirring to combine. Carefully pour over the chicken. Cover the casserole and cook in the oven for 1 hour. Blend the cornflour with the lemon juice and 1 tablespoon of cold water and stir into the casserole. Return to the oven for a further 10 minutes or until the chicken is cooked and the vegetables are tender. Remove the bay leaves and stir in the chopped parsley. Garnish the chicken with the flat-leaf parsley. Serve with mashed potatoes and vegetables.

Ingredients   SERVES 4

4 chicken joints, skinned
125 g/4 oz pitted dried prunes
2 bay leaves
12 shallots
2 tsp olive oil
125 g/4 oz small button
    mushrooms, wiped
1 tsp soft dark brown sugar
$^1/_2$ tsp wholegrain mustard
2 tsp tomato purée
150 ml/$^1/_4$ pint light ale
150 ml/$^1/_4$ pint chicken stock
salt and freshly ground
    black pepper
2 tsp cornflour
2 tsp lemon juice
2 tbsp chopped fresh parsley
flat-leaf parsley, to garnish

To serve:

mashed potatoes
seasonal green vegetables

Nutritional details per 100 g   energy 89 kcals/377 kj • protein 10 g • carbohydrate 8 g • fat 2 g • fibre 1.6 g • sugar 4.3 g • sodium 0.1 g

✓ cow's milk-free   ✓ egg-free   ● gluten-free   ● wheat-free   ✓ nut-free   ● vegetarian   ● vegan   ✓ seafood-free

Coconut Fish Curry

1 Put 1 tablespoon of the oil into a large frying pan and cook the onion, pepper and garlic for 5 minutes, or until soft. Add the remaining oil, curry paste, ginger and chilli and cook for a further minute.

2 Pour in the coconut milk and bring to the boil, reduce the heat and simmer gently for 5 minutes, stirring occasionally. Add the monkfish to the pan and continue to simmer gently for 5–10 minutes, or until the fish is tender but not overcooked.

3 Meanwhile, cook the rice in a saucepan of boiling salted water for 15 minutes, or until tender. Drain the rice thoroughly and turn out into a serving dish.

4 Stir the chopped coriander and chutney gently into the fish curry and season to taste with salt and pepper. Spoon the fish curry over the cooked rice, garnish with lime wedges and coriander sprigs and serve immediately with spoonfuls of Greek yogurt (avoid if intolerant of ewe's milk) and warm naan bread.

Ingredients   SERVES 4

2 tbsp sunflower oil
1 medium onion, peeled and very
  finely chopped
1 yellow pepper, deseeded and
  finely chopped
1 garlic clove, peeled and crushed
1 tbsp mild curry paste
2.5 cm/1 inch piece root ginger,
  peeled and grated
1 red chilli, deseeded and
  finely chopped
400 ml can coconut milk
700 g/1½ lb firm white fish,
  e.g. monkfish fillets, skinned
  and cut into chunks
225 g/8 oz basmati rice
1 tbsp freshly chopped coriander
1 tbsp mango chutney
salt and freshly ground black pepper

To serve:

lime wedges; fresh coriander sprigs,
ewe's milk Greek yogurt; warm naan

Nutritional details per 100 g energy 139 kcals/583 kj • protein 9 g • carbohydrate 19 g • fat 3 g • fibre 0.4 g • sugar 2.6 g • sodium 0.2 g

✓ cow's milk-free   ✓ egg-free   ● gluten-free   ● wheat-free   ✓ nut-free   ● vegetarian   ● vegan   ● seafood-free

Courgette & Tarragon Tortilla

1   Peel the potatoes and slice thinly. Dry the slices on a clean tea towel to get them as dry as possible. Heat the oil in a large heavy-based pan, add the onion and cook for 3 minutes. Add the potatoes with a little salt and pepper, then stir the potatoes and onion lightly to coat in the oil.

2   Reduce the heat to the lowest possible setting, cover and cook gently for 5 minutes. Turn the potatoes and onion over and continue to cook for a further 5 minutes. Give the pan a shake every now and again to ensure that the potatoes do not stick to the base or burn. Add the courgette, then cover and cook for a further 10 minutes.

3   Beat the eggs and tarragon together and season to taste with salt and pepper. Pour the egg mixture over the vegetables and return to the heat. Cook on a low heat for up to 20–25 minutes, or until there is no liquid egg left on the surface of the tortilla.

4   Turn the tortilla over by inverting it onto the lid or onto a flat plate. Return the pan to the heat and cook for a final 3–5 minutes, or until the underside is golden brown. If preferred, place the tortilla under a preheated grill for 4 minutes, or until set and golden brown on top. Cut into small squares and serve hot or cold with tomato wedges.

Ingredients   SERVES 6

700 g/1½ lb potatoes
3 tbsp olive oil
1 onion, peeled and thinly sliced
salt and freshly ground
   black pepper
1 courgette, trimmed and
   thinly sliced
6 medium eggs
2 tbsp freshly chopped tarragon
tomato wedges, to serve

Nutritional details per 100 g   energy 118 kcals/496 kj · protein 4 g · carbohydrate 15 g · fat 5 g · fibre 1.3 g · sugar 1.5 g · sodium trace
✓ cow's milk-free   egg-free   ✓ gluten-free   ✓ wheat-free   ✓ nut-free   ✓ vegetarian   vegan   ✓ seafood-free

Fried Ginger Rice with Soy-glazed Duck

1 Put the duck slices in a bowl with 1 tablespoon of the soy sauce, the mirin, 1 teaspoon of the sugar and one third of the ginger. Stir, then leave to stand.

2 Heat 2 tablespoons of the oil in a large, heavy-based saucepan. Add the garlic and half the remaining ginger and stir-fry for 1 minute. Add the rice and cook for 3 minutes, stirring constantly, until translucent.

3 Stir in all but 125 ml/4 fl oz of the stock, with 1 teaspoon of the soy sauce, and bring to the boil. Season with pepper. Reduce the heat to very low and simmer, covered, for 25–30 minutes until the rice is tender and the liquid is absorbed. Cover and leave to stand.

4 Heat the remaining oil in a large frying pan or wok. Drain the duck strips and add to the frying pan. Stir-fry for 2–3 minutes until just coloured. Add 1 tablespoon of soy sauce and the remaining sugar and cook for 1 minute until glazed. Transfer to a plate and keep warm.

5 Stir in the ham, mangetout, spring onions, the remaining ginger and the chopped coriander. Add the remaining stock and duck marinade and cook until the liquid is almost reduced. Fork in the rice and chilli sauce to taste, if using, and stir well. Turn into a serving dish and top with the duck. Garnish with coriander sprigs and serve immediately.

Ingredients SERVES 4–6

2 duck breasts, skinned and diagonally
   cut into thin slices
2–3 tbsp Japanese soy sauce
1 tbsp mirin (sweet rice wine) or sherry
2 tbsp brown sugar
5 cm/2 inch piece fresh root ginger,
   peeled and finely chopped
4 tbsp vegetable oil
2 garlic cloves, peeled and crushed
300 g/11 oz long-grain brown rice
900 ml/1½ pints chicken stock
freshly ground black pepper
125 g/4 oz lean ham, diced
175 g/6 oz mangetout,
   diagonally cut in half
8 spring onions, trimmed and thinly
   sliced diagonally
1 tbsp freshly chopped coriander
sweet or hot chilli sauce,
   to taste (optional)
sprigs of fresh coriander,
   to garnish

Nutritional details per 100 g energy 158 kcals/660 kj • protein 10 g • carbohydrate 12 g • fat 8 g • fibre 0.5 g • sugar 4.8 g • sodium 0.6 g

✓ cow's milk-free   ✓ egg-free   ● gluten-free   ● wheat-free   ✓ nut-free   ● vegetarian   ● vegan   ✓ seafood-free

Fruits de Mer Stir-fry

1   Prepare the shellfish. Peel the prawns and, if necessary, remove the thin black veins from their backs. Lightly rinse the squid rings and clean the scallops if necessary. Remove and discard any mussels that are open. Scrub and de-beard the remaining mussels, removing any barnacles from the shells. Cover the mussels with cold water until required.

2   Peel the root ginger and either grate coarsely or shred finely with a sharp knife and place into a small bowl.

3   Add the garlic and chillies to the small bowl, pour in the soy sauce and mix well.

4   Place the mixed shellfish, except the mussels, in a bowl and pour over the marinade. Stir, cover and leave for 15 minutes.

5   Heat a wok until hot, then add the oil and heat until almost smoking. Add the prepared vegetables, stir-fry for 3 minutes, then stir in the plum sauce.

6   Add the shellfish and the mussels with the marinade and stir-fry for a further 3–4 minutes, or until the fish is cooked. Discard any mussels that have not opened. Garnish with the spring onions and serve immediately with the freshly cooked rice.

Ingredients   SERVES 4

450 g/1 lb mixed fresh shellfish,
   such as tiger prawns, squid,
   scallops and mussels
2.5 cm/1 inch piece fresh root ginger
2 garlic cloves, peeled and crushed
2 green chillies, deseeded and
   finely chopped
3 tbsp light soy sauce
2 tbsp olive oil
200 g/7 oz baby sweetcorn, rinsed
200 g/7 oz asparagus tips,
   trimmed and cut in half widthways
200 g/7 oz mangetout, trimmed
2 tbsp plum sauce
4 spring onions, trimmed
   and shredded, to garnish
freshly cooked rice, to serve

Nutritional details per 100 g   energy 87 kcals/367 kj • protein 7 g • carbohydrate 10 g • fat 2 g • fibre 0.7 g • sugar 1 g • sodium 0.6 g

✓ cow's milk-free   ✓ egg-free   ◐ gluten-free   ◐ wheat-free   ✓ nut-free   ◐ vegetarian   ◐ vegan   ◐ seafood-free

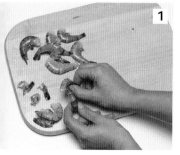
1

3

6

Haddock with an Olive Crust

1 Preheat the oven to 190°C/375°F/Gas Mark 5. Place the black olives in a small bowl with the breadcrumbs and add the chopped tarragon.

2 Add the garlic to the olives with the chopped spring onions and the olive oil. Mix together lightly.

3 Wipe the fillets with either a clean damp cloth or damp kitchen paper, then place on a lightly oiled baking sheet.

4 Place spoonfuls of the olive and breadcrumb mixture on top of each fillet and press the mixture down lightly and evenly over the top of the fish.

5 Bake the fish in the preheated oven for 20–25 minutes or until the fish is cooked thoroughly and the topping is golden brown. Serve immediately with the freshly cooked carrots and beans.

Ingredients   SERVES 4

12 pitted black olives, finely chopped
75 g/3 oz fresh white breadcrumbs
1 tbsp freshly chopped tarragon
1 garlic clove, peeled and crushed
3 spring onions, trimmed and
    finely chopped
1 tbsp olive oil
4 x 175 g/6 oz thick skinless
    haddock fillets

To serve:
freshly cooked carrots
freshly cooked beans

Nutritional details per 100 g energy 93 kcals/394 kj · protein 13 g · carbohydrate 6 g · fat 2 g · fibre 1.2 g · sugar 1.1 g · sodium 0.2 g

✓ cow's milk-free   ✓ egg-free   ● gluten-free   ● wheat-free   ✓ nut-free   ● vegetarian   ● vegan   ● seafood-free

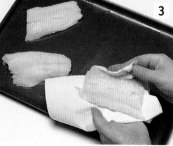

Hoisin Chicken Pancakes

1 Preheat the oven to 190°C/375°F/Gas Mark 5. In a non–metallic bowl, mix the hoisin sauce with the garlic, ginger, soy sauce, sesame oil and seasoning.

2 Add the chicken thighs and turn to coat in the mixture. Cover loosely and leave in the refrigerator to marinate for 3–4 hours, turning the chicken from time to time.

3 Remove the chicken from the marinade and place in a roasting tin. Reserve the marinade. Bake in the preheated oven for 30 minutes, basting occasionally with the marinade.

4 Cut the cucumber in half lengthways and remove the seeds by running a teaspoon down the middle to scoop them out. Cut into thin batons.

5 Place the pancakes in a steamer to warm or heat according to packet instructions. Thinly slice the hot chicken and arrange on a plate with the shredded spring onions, cucumber and pancakes.

6 Place a spoonful of the chicken in the middle of each warmed pancake and top with pieces of cucumber, spring onion and a little dipping sauce. Roll up and serve immediately.

Ingredients   SERVES 4

3 tbsp hoisin sauce
1 garlic clove, peeled and crushed
2.5 cm/1 inch piece root ginger,
    peeled and finely grated
1 tbsp soy sauce
1 tsp sesame oil
salt and freshly ground black pepper
4 skinless chicken thighs
$^1/_2$ cucumber, peeled (optional)
12 bought Chinese pancakes
6 spring onions, trimmed and cut
    lengthways into fine shreds
sweet chilli dipping sauce,
    to serve

Nutritional details per 100 g   energy 184 kcals/780 kj • protein 21 g • carbohydrate 21 g • fat 2 g • fibre 0.8 g • sugar 0.7 g • sodium 0.4 g

✓ cow's milk-free   ✓ egg-free   ⬤ gluten-free   ⬤ wheat-free   ✓ nut-free   ⬤ vegetarian   ⬤ vegan   ✓ seafood-free

2

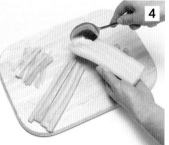
4

5

Oriental Minced Chicken on Rocket & Tomato

1 Finely chop the shallots and garlic. Cut the carrot into matchsticks, slice the water chestnuts thinly and reserve. Heat the oil in a wok or large, heavy-based frying pan and add the chicken. Stir-fry for 3–4 minutes over a moderately high heat, breaking up any large pieces of chicken.

2 Add the garlic and shallots and cook for 2–3 minutes until softened. Sprinkle over the Chinese five-spice powder and the chilli powder and continue to cook for about 1 minute.

3 Add the carrot, water chestnuts, soy and fish sauces and 2 tablespoons of water. Stir-fry for a further 2 minutes. Remove from the heat and reserve to cool slightly.

4 Deseed the tomatoes and cut into thin wedges. Toss with the rocket and divide between four serving plates. Spoon the warm chicken mixture over the rocket and tomato wedges and serve immediately to prevent the rocket from wilting.

Ingredients   SERVES 4

2 shallots, peeled
1 garlic clove, peeled
1 carrot, peeled
50 g/2 oz water chestnuts
1 tsp oil
350 g/12 oz fresh chicken mince
1 tsp Chinese five-spice powder
pinch chilli powder
1 tsp soy sauce
1 tbsp fish sauce
8 cherry tomatoes
50 g/2 oz rocket

Nutritional details per 100 g energy 105 kcals/442 kj • protein 15 g • carbohydrate 4 g • fat 3 g • fibre 0.4 g • sugar 1.1 g • sodium 0.3 g

✓ cow's milk-free   ✓ egg-free   ◐ gluten-free   ◐ wheat-free   ✓ nut-free   ◐ vegetarian   ◐ vegan   ◐ seafood-free

1

1

4

Pan-cooked Chicken with Thai Spices

1 Lightly bruise the kaffir lime leaves and put into a bowl with the chopped ginger. Pour over the chicken stock, cover and leave to infuse for 30 minutes.

2 Meanwhile, cut each chicken breast into two pieces. Heat the oil in a large, non-stick frying pan or flameproof casserole and brown the chicken pieces for 2–3 minutes on each side.

3 Strain the infused chicken stock into the pan. Half cover the pan with a lid and gently simmer for 10 minutes.

4 Stir in the coconut milk, fish sauce and chopped chillies. Simmer uncovered for 5–6 minutes, or until the chicken is tender and cooked through and the sauce has reduced slightly.

5 Meanwhile, cook the rice in boiling salted water according to the packet instructions. Drain the rice thoroughly.

6 Stir the lime juice and chopped coriander into the sauce. Season to taste with salt and pepper. Serve the chicken and sauce on a bed of rice. Garnish with wedges of lime and freshly chopped coriander and serve immediately.

Ingredients   SERVES 4

4 kaffir lime leaves
5 cm/2 inch piece of root ginger, peeled and chopped
300 ml/¹/₂ pint chicken stock, boiling
4 x 175 g/6 oz chicken breasts
2 tsp groundnut oil
5 tbsp coconut milk
1 tbsp fish sauce
2 red chillies, deseeded and finely chopped
225 g/8 oz Thai jasmine rice
1 tbsp lime juice
3 tbsp freshly chopped coriander
salt and freshly ground black pepper

To garnish:

wedges of lime
freshly chopped coriander

Nutritional details per 100 g   energy 133 kcals/560 kj · protein 21 g · carbohydrate 8 g · fat 2 g · fibre 0.4 g · sugar trace · sodium 0.3 g

✓ cow's milk-free   ✓ egg-free   ● gluten-free   ● wheat-free   ● nut-free   ● vegetarian   ● vegan   ● seafood-free

1

2

4

Prawn & Chilli Soup

1   To make spring onion curls, finely shred the spring onions lengthways. Place in a bowl of iced cold water and reserve.

2   Remove the heads and shells from the prawns, leaving the tails intact.

3   Split the prawns almost in two to form a butterfly shape and individually remove the black thread that runs down the back of each one.

4   In a large pan, heat the stock with the lime rind and juice, fish sauce, chilli and soy sauce.

5   Bruise the lemon grass by crushing it along its length with a rolling pin, then add to the stock mixture.

6   When the stock mixture is boiling, add the prawns and cook until they are pink.

7   Remove the lemon grass and add the rice vinegar and coriander.

8   Ladle into bowls and garnish with the spring onion curls. Serve immediately.

Ingredients   SERVES 4

2 spring onions, trimmed
225 g/8 oz whole raw tiger prawns
750 ml/1¼ pints fish stock
juice and finely grated rind of 1 lime
1 tbsp fish sauce
1 red chilli, deseeded and chopped
1 tbsp soy sauce
1 lemon grass stalk
2 tbsp rice vinegar
4 tbsp freshly chopped coriander

Nutritional details per 100 g energy 72 kcals/304 kj • protein 13 g • carbohydrate 4 g • fat 1 g • fibre trace • sugar 0.5 g • sodium 1.2 g

✓ cow's milk-free   ✓ egg-free   gluten-free   wheat-free   ✓ nut-free   vegetarian   vegan   seafood-free

1

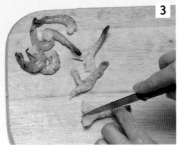

3

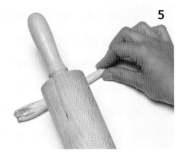

5

Royal Fried Rice

1   Place the rice in a sieve, rinse with cold water, then drain. Place in a saucepan and add twice the volume of water, stirring briefly. Bring to the boil, cover and simmer gently for 15 minutes without further stirring. If the rice has fully absorbed the water while covered, add a little more water. Continue to simmer, uncovered, for another 5 minutes or until the rice is fully cooked and the water has evaporated. Leave to cool.

2   Place the eggs, sesame oil and a pinch of salt in a small bowl. Using a fork, mix just to break the egg. Reserve.

3   Heat a wok and add 1 tablespoon of the vegetable oil. When very hot, stir-fry the peppers, onion and sweetcorn for 2 minutes or until the onion is soft. Remove the vegetables and reserve.

4   Clean the wok and add the remaining oil. When very hot, add the cold cooked rice and stir-fry for 3 minutes, or until it is heated through. Drizzle in the egg mixture and continue to stir-fry for 2–3 minutes or until the eggs have set. Add the prawns and crabmeat to the rice. Stir-fry for 1 minute. Season to taste with salt and pepper and add the sugar with the soy sauce. Stir to mix and spoon into a warmed serving dish. Garnish with a radish flower and sprinkle with freshly snipped and whole chives. Serve immediately.

Ingredients   SERVES 4

450 g/1 lb Thai fragrant rice
2 large eggs
2 tsp sesame oil
salt and freshly ground black pepper
3 tbsp vegetable oil
1 red pepper, deseeded and
   finely diced
1 yellow pepper, deseeded and
   finely diced
1 green pepper, deseeded and
   finely diced
2 red onions, peeled and diced
125 g/4 oz sweetcorn kernels
125 g/4 oz cooked peeled prawns,
   thawed if frozen
125 g/4 oz white crabmeat,
   drained if canned
$1/4$ tsp sugar
2 tsp light soy sauce

To garnish:

radish roses
freshly snipped and whole chive leaves

Nutritional details per 100 g energy 107 kcals/445 kj • protein 5 g • carbohydrate 13 g • fat 4 g • fibre 0.1 g • sugar 0.9 g • sodium 0.3 g

✓ cow's milk-free   egg-free   gluten-free   wheat-free   ✓ nut-free   vegetarian   vegan   seafood-free

Salmon Teriyaki with Noodles & Crispy Greens

1 Cut the salmon into paper–thin slices and place in a shallow dish. Mix together the soy sauce, mirin or sherry, sake and ginger. Pour over the salmon, cover and leave to marinate for 15–30 minutes.

2 Remove and discard the thick stalks from the spring greens. Lay several leaves on top of each other, roll up tightly, then shred finely. Pour in enough oil to cover about 5 cm/2 inches of the wok. Deep–fry the greens in batches for about 1 minute each until crisp. Remove and drain on absorbent kitchen paper. Transfer to a serving dish, sprinkle with salt and sugar and toss together.

3 Place the noodles in a bowl and pour over warm water to cover. Leave to soak for 15–20 minutes until soft, then drain. With scissors, cut into 15 cm/6 inch lengths. Remove the salmon slices from the marinade, reserving the marinade for later, and arrange them in a single layer on a baking sheet. Grill for about 2 minutes until lightly cooked, without turning.

4 When the oil in the wok is cool enough, tip most of it away, leaving about 1 tablespoon. Heat until hot, then add the noodles and the reserved marinade and stir–fry for 3–4 minutes. Tip the noodles into a large, warmed serving bowl and arrange the salmon slices on top, garnished with chopped dill, sprigs of fresh dill and lemon zest. Scatter with a little of the crispy greens and serve the rest separately.

Ingredients   SERVES 4

350 g/12 oz salmon fillet
3 tbsp Japanese soy sauce
3 tbsp mirin or sweet sherry
3 tbsp sake
1 tbsp freshly grated root ginger
225 g/8 oz spring greens
vegetable oil for deep–frying
pinch of salt
$^1/_2$ tsp caster sugar
125 g/4 oz flat rice noodles

To garnish:

1 tbsp freshly chopped dill
sprigs of fresh dill
zest of $^1/_2$ lemon

Nutritional details per 100 g   energy 196 kcals/813 kj ● protein 12 g ● carbohydrate 6 g ● fat 14 g ● fibre 0.9 g ● sugar 1.5 g ● sodium 0.5 g

✓ cow's milk-free   ✓ egg-free   ● gluten-free   ● wheat-free   ✓ nut-free   ● vegetarian   ● vegan   ● seafood-free

1

2

4

Shredded Beef in Hoisin Sauce

1 Trim the celery and peel the carrots, then cut into fine matchsticks and reserve.

2 Place the steak between two sheets of greaseproof paper or baking parchment. Beat the steak with a meat mallet or rolling pin until very thin, then slice into strips. Season the cornflour with salt and pepper and use to coat the steak. Reserve.

3 Heat a wok, add the oil and, when hot, add the spring onions and cook for 1 minute, then add the steak and stir-fry for a further 3–4 minutes, or until the meat is sealed.

4 Add the celery and carrot matchsticks to the wok and stir-fry for a further 2 minutes before adding the soy, hoisin and chilli sauces and the sherry. Bring to the boil and simmer for 2–3 minutes, or until the steak is tender and the vegetables are cooked.

5 Plunge the fine egg noodles into boiling water and leave for 4 minutes. Drain, then spoon onto a large serving dish. Top with the cooked shredded steak, then sprinkle with chopped coriander and serve immediately.

Ingredients SERVES 4

2 celery sticks
125 g/4 oz carrots
450 g/1 lb rump steak
2 tbsp cornflour
salt and freshly ground black pepper
2 tbsp sunflower oil
4 spring onions, trimmed
    and chopped
2 tbsp light soy sauce
1 tbsp hoisin sauce
1 tbsp sweet chilli sauce
2 tbsp dry sherry
250 g pack fine egg thread noodles
1 tbsp freshly chopped coriander

Nutritional details per 100 g energy 151 kcals/633 kj • protein 14 g • carbohydrate 10 g • fat 6 g • fibre 0.6 g • sugar 1 g • sodium 0.3 g

✓ cow's milk-free • egg-free • gluten-free • wheat-free • ✓ nut-free • vegetarian • vegan • ✓ seafood-free

Smoked Turkey Tagliatelle

1 Heat the oil in a saucepan. Add the spring onions and garlic and cook gently for 2–3 minutes until beginning to soften. Stir in the sliced courgette and cook for 1 minute.

2 Add the wine and let it bubble for 1–2 minutes. Stir in the chopped tomatoes, bring to the boil and simmer uncovered over a low heat for 15 minutes, or until the courgettes are tender and the sauce slightly reduced. Stir the shredded basil into the sauce and season to taste with salt and pepper.

3 Meanwhile, bring a large pan of salted water to the boil. Add the tagliatelle and cook for 10 minutes, until 'al dente' or according to the packet instructions. Drain thoroughly.

4 Return the tagliatelle to the pan, add half the tomato sauce and toss together to coat the pasta thoroughly in the sauce. Cover with a lid and reserve.

5 Add the strips of turkey to the remaining sauce and heat gently for 2–3 minutes until piping hot.

6 Divide the tagliatelle among four serving plates. Spoon over the sauce, garnish with basil leaves and serve immediately.

Ingredients   SERVES 4

2 tsp olive oil

1 bunch spring onions, trimmed
and diagonally sliced

1 garlic clove, peeled and crushed

1 small courgette, trimmed, cut in
half lengthways and sliced

4 tbsp dry white wine

400 g can chopped tomatoes

2 tbsp freshly shredded basil

salt and freshly ground
black pepper

225 g/8 oz spinach and
egg tagliatelle

225 g/8 oz smoked turkey breast,
cut into strips

small fresh basil leaves,
to garnish

Nutritional details per 100 g   energy 79 kcals/334 kj • protein 8 g • carbohydrate 7 g • fat 2 g • fibre 0.5 g • sugar 1.4 g • sodium 0.3 g

✓ cow's milk-free   egg-free   gluten-free   wheat-free   ✓ nut-free   vegetarian   vegan   ✓ seafood-free

Sweet-&-Sour Rice with Chicken

1 Trim the spring onions, then cut lengthways into fine strips. Drop into a large bowl of iced water and reserve.

2 Mix together the sesame oil and Chinese five–spice powder and use to rub into the cubed chicken. Heat the wok, then add the oil and, when hot, cook the garlic and onion for 2–3 minutes, or until transparent and softened.

3 Add the chicken and stir-fry over a medium–high heat until the chicken is golden and cooked through. Using a slotted spoon, remove from the wok and keep warm.

4 Stir the rice into the wok and add the water, tomato ketchup, tomato purée, honey, vinegar and soy sauce. Stir well to mix. Bring to the boil, then simmer until almost all of the liquid is absorbed. Stir in the carrot and reserved chicken and continue to cook for 3–4 minutes.

5 Drain the spring onions, which will have become curly. Garnish the rice and chicken the spring onion curls and serve immediately.

Ingredients   SERVES 4

4 spring onions
2 tsp sesame oil
1 tsp Chinese five–spice powder
450 g/1 lb chicken breast,
    cut into cubes
1 tbsp vegetable oil
1 garlic clove, peeled and crushed
1 medium onion, peeled and
    sliced into thin wedges
225 g/8 oz long–grain white rice
600 ml/1 pint water
4 tbsp tomato ketchup
1 tbsp tomato purée
2 tbsp honey
1 tbsp vinegar
1 tbsp dark soy sauce
1 carrot, peeled and cut
    into matchsticks

Nutritional details per 100 g energy 126 kcals/528 kj • protein 14 g • carbohydrate 12 g • fat 3 g • fibre 0.5 g • sugar 5.7 g • sodium 0.2 g

✓ cow's milk-free   ✓ egg-free   ◉ gluten-free   ◉ wheat-free   ✓ nut-free   ◉ vegetarian   ◉ vegan   ✓ seafood-free

Index